RUTH

BOOKS BY

IRVING FINEMAN

RUTH

JACOB

DOCTOR ADDAMS

HEAR YE SONS

LOVERS MUST LEARN

THIS PURE YOUNG MAN

•

Ruth

by IRVING FINEMAN

HARPER & BROTHERS, PUBLISHERS

NEW YORK

TO MY SON

JONATHAN

RUTH

And it came to pass in the days when the judges judged, that there was a famine in the land. And a certain man of Bethlehem in Judah went to sojourn in the land of Moab, he and his wife and his two sons. And the name of the man was Elimelech, and the name of his wife Naomi, and the name of his two sons Mahlon and Chilion. . . . And they came into the country of Moab, and continued there. And Elimelech Naomi's husband died; and she was left and her two sons. And they took them wives of the women of Moab, and the name of the one was Orpah and the name of the other Ruth. And they dwelled there about ten years. And Mahlon and Chilion died both of them. . . .

RUTH

THE GRAVES of the three men of Judah were on a bare windy knoll on the outskirts of the ancient fortified City of Moab, set apart from the Baal-guarded burial ground of the Moabites. The three low mounds of whitewashed masonry, each marked with the lion of Judah and with the male pillar upraised at its head, were enclosed by a low stone wall.

And the three women, the old one all in black raiment and the two young ones in white with black headcloths, their shadows long in the late sunlight, were tending that mournful place, plucking the weeds and adorning the tombs with fresh flowers.

> *For, lo, the winter is past,*
> *The rain is over and gone;*
> *The flowers appear on the earth,*

Naomi sang softly as she unbent from her task and lifted her wise old eyes from the grave of Elimelech to look westward across the high grassy plains of Moab.

> *The time of the singing of birds is come,*
> *And the voice of the turtle is heard in our land,*

sang Naomi, raising her voice in a quavering chant as she stood gazing across the gap where the Salt Sea lay—and beyond, to the distant hills of Judah, dark blue against the flaming sunset sky—to her beloved hills of the land of

Israel, whose crests the keen eyes in that timeworn face searched for something.

"What seest thou there, Naomi?" asked Ruth, going to stand beside her, carrying the many-colored windflowers—the bright anemones and the poppies they had gathered in the fields to put in the painted jars by the tombs. Ruth spoke in the ancient manner of the Moabites, her voice flowing slowly like honey; and on her beautiful brow, beneath the widow's headcloth gleamed a row of golden amulets such as the daughters of princes in Moab wore. Each coin bore the figure of Ashtar crowned with a crescent moon and stars and offering her full round breasts. And, with the spring breeze fluttering the clothing of her sweetly rounded yet sturdy form, Ruth, beside the thin, withered and wintry figure of Naomi, was the embodiment of ripe summer to come. Ruth raised her hand to shade her soft dark eyes from the sun. "I can see nothing, Naomi," she said.

"When you are old," said Naomi, "you see better what is far off than what is near." She glanced at Ruth's sweet face and smiled. "And so, too, the past and the future are clearer to the old than is the present, which is all that the young can see. Sometimes," said Naomi peering again at the distant hills, "sometimes there northward against the light of the setting sun it seems to me I can see Jerusalem, which is Jebus, the mighty walled city of the Jebusites, and even Bethlehem in Judah, my home." And she sighed. "You have never been away from home, Ruth."

Ruth shook her head, and looked with compassion into those old eyes so full of longing.

"Ten years is a long time," said Naomi sadly. "And I long for my homeland, whose ways are different from the ways of Moab."

2

And Ruth, looking curiously at her mother-in-law, said: "Tell me, Naomi, why hast thou been content so long to remain in Moab and why didst thou put aside the ways of Israel of which Mahlon often told me, seeing that thou hast not taken on all the ways of Moab in these ten years?"

Naomi said: "You have yet to learn, my daughter, that a woman will remain content in any place so long as the man she loves is there. In our Book of Remembrance it is said: *A man shall leave his father and his mother, and shall cleave unto his wife;* but it is the other way round— it is we who cleave to them. And I loved my Elimelech; and he put aside the ways of Israel here for fear of arousing the hatred of the men of Moab, who tolerated him only for his wealth and the cattle he brought with him into the land, although he did not take to their ways. Thus does a man who is not free to live according to his lights give up his spirit before the death of his body. And now that he is gone and our two sons also, my spirit longs to return to Bethlehem in Judah and the ways of Israel. Only yesterday I heard a camel driver who had come from the west, from the land of Israel, say that the famine is over in Judah. The Lord God of Israel has returned to his people and given them bread; and they will have a good harvest this year."

And Ruth said: "Tell me now, Naomi, of Bethlehem in Judah—what manner of city is it? . . ." And both women, the old and the young, stood absorbed in their talk of that far-off place, so that neither one heard the first thin strains of music wafted down to them on the warm evening wind.

But Orpah heard. Orpah raised her pretty face from the flowers she was setting on Chilion's grave, and turned her petulant painted eyes up toward the twilit city on the hill-

3

side, toward its multitude of flat-roofed sun-baked houses threaded by narrow streets and dominated by its massive square stone citadel and its high place. It was there that the eager eyes of Orpah came to rest. For it was from there, from the altared green grove of the gods of Moab—of bloodthirsty Chemosh, of sensual Baal-Peor and fertile Ashtar his wife, whose tall phallic pillars and bloodstained stones of sacrifice glowed red in the setting sun—that the mounting music came, its thin languorous wailing pulsing now with the blood-stirring beat of drums. . . . And Orpah rose to her feet, trembling with excitement, and cried out like a child: "It is the call to the first rites of spring!"

But Ruth put a restraining hand upon Orpah's arm and raised a warning finger to her lips, quieting Orpah for the sake of Naomi, whose old eyes changed from longing to wrathfulness as she turned and watched with them how that strange music roused up the City of Moab.

The doors of its crowded clay houses opened; the men and the women poured out into the dusty streets, streaming along their crooked courses like the dark waters of freshets filling dry brook beds, gathering at their corners into growing throngs; each to be led by a painted priest of Baal tricked out in women's robes hung with tinkling silver bells and brandishing his bright blade before a sacrificial litter. And the people were all shouting and singing, drinking from wine skins and drunkenly dancing as they wound their way out of the city and up the paths to the high place, whose wild music their wilder voices all but drowned out—the shrill voices of the women:

> We are women, the wives of Baal,
> Our lips are sweet, sweet as the pomegranate,
> With them is kissing and conception in embracing,
> She who is passionate shall bring forth seed . . .

4

and the seductive voices of the priests:

> I will summon the gods, gracious and beautiful,
> Come drink wine with me, my weary ones!

One of the throngs came pouring along the path which curved by the foot of the knoll where Naomi and Ruth and Orpah stood. As the head of the procession approached they could see the bearers of the sacrifice, sodden men holding writhing snakes. And behind it came women bearing doves and full-breasted figures of Ashtar with the serpent writhing upon her; and they came dancing lasciviously with their own breasts bared, but for one woman, disheveled and wailing piteously. And as it came nearer still they saw what was on the garlanded litter—a naked child, a fat infant wearing a chaplet of flowers on its curly head, laughing and crowing and waving its dimpled hands to its wailing mother and to the drunken crowd, unmindful that they were taking it up to be sacrificed to their gods—the gods of force, of fornication and fertility; unmindful that the bright blade in the hands of the gaudy, jingling priest dancing before the litter was meant for its little heart.

Then came a drab mob of Moabites led by two huge men, tall twin brothers alike in their rude strength and richly dressed in the raiment of princes, and they shouted in turn to the three women by the graves on the knoll:

"How long will you mourn those dead men of Judah?"

"Come Ruth, come Orpah, you are not Israelites; have you forgotten that you are daughters of our house—the house of King Eglon? So come with us up to the high place!"

"We are alive and lusty, and after the warm blood spurts from the babe on the stone of Chemosh, we will drink wine and dance and make love in the grove of Ashtar, Queen of Heaven."

"Come Orpah, come Ruth, it is spring! Come serve Baal-Peor and Ashtar, the moon goddess, or you will dry out and shrivel up like old Naomi, the woman of Judah. . . ."

To their seductive calls Ruth gave no heed nor answer. Though inwardly trembling, straight and proudly beautiful Ruth stood, holding Orpah to her, protecting like a younger sister poor Orpah who, though she was older than Ruth, seemed still childlike; Orpah, who had been so gay and affectionate, was lonesome and lost without her lusty Chilion. And even now as she clung to Ruth, Orpah looked out with curious eyes, half frightened and half fascinated, upon that host of hot-blooded men and wanton women obscenely chanting as they staggered and danced on up the hill to the altared high place and its green grove.

But Naomi did not remain silent. Naomi gave heed and answer to their mockery: "Go on, you murderers of Moab! Killers of your own first-born! Go wallow in your swinishness! . . ." Like an angry prophetess Naomi stood and called down the wrath of the Lord God of Israel upon their iniquities.

And they jeered as they passed and taunted her, calling her "old witch of Judah" and inviting her to come up and watch their revelry in the grove since she was far too old to take part in it. "Or go back whence thou camest," the twin princes yelled, "and leave our women to us!"

"You have reason to fear the women of Judah," cried Naomi, "you foul despoilers of women! Is it because you have heard of the victory of our Deborah over the Canaanites and how Jael killed their general Sisera that you fear to have an old woman of Judah among you? Is it because you fear that your women, too, may become strong and refuse to give up their young, their first-born, to the priests and the princes who hold them in beastly bondage and——"

From the high place came the sudden blast of a ram's horn followed by the shrill bloodcurdling scream of an infant in mortal pain.

"They have begun the sacrifices!" shouted the two princes; and the mob in frenzy turned from Naomi and went hurrying after them up the hill, where the blood-red sunlight stained the faces of the crowd pressed close around one of the sacrificial stones as the priest's flashing blade rose and fell.

And as that dreadful childish wail died away the old woman on the knoll turned to the two young ones, the wrath in her eyes changed to unspeakable horror and loathing. "I can bear the abominations of Moab no longer," said Naomi to Ruth and Orpah. "I must return to the land of Israel, to Bethlehem in Judah." Then she turned to the three graves. "Farewell, Elimelech, my husband. And farewell, my sons. Would that I could take you back to the land of your fathers—of Abraham and Isaac and Jacob." And she stood looking again to the distant hills, dim now in the failing light. Then she returned to Ruth and Orpah. And there were tears in her old eyes. "I love you dearly, my daughters, and it grieves me to leave you. But you see how it is with me here. I must go now and prepare for my difficult journey."

"But surely," said Ruth, "thou wilt not go now with night coming!"

"Indeed," said Naomi, "I must go now; for I have angered the revelers and they may do me harm when they return from the high place, now that there is no man to protect me. You will come and say farewell to me, will you not?"

And they nodded, too moved to speak, and watched her descend the knoll, her spare old figure so straight, her glance so fearless that the last of the straggling revelers on the road made way for her as she went by them to return to her house.

Then Ruth said to her sister-in-law: "We cannot let her go alone. I think I shall go with Naomi to Judah. Thou wilt come, too, wilt thou not, Orpah?"

But Orpah looked frightened: "All that dangerous way to a strange country—to live among strangers? Dost thou not fear to go, Ruth?"

The beat of the drums and the screaming of revelers and sacrificial victims drifted down to them in wild confusion from the high place, where torches were being lit against the fast-falling darkness.

And Ruth said: "I do indeed fear to go. But can we stay here . . . ?" And she turned to the grave of Mahlon. "Thou wouldst not have me stay, my beloved husband."

"It is only," said Orpah eagerly, "that we are unaccustomed to the ways of our people because of our marriage to the men of Judah who did not do so—except that one time when Chilion took me up to the high place. It was exciting, Ruth," she whispered, "though Chilion would not let me take part and I did nothing—only looked on and saw how——" And seeing the aversion in Ruth's dark eyes, she said: "But if we married men of Moab we should soon get used to . . ."

But Ruth shook her head. "Nay, I cannot let Naomi go that long way alone. I shall go with her."

"And leave me here?" cried Orpah, clinging to Ruth.

8

"Thou knowest how unhappy I would be without thee, Ruth. Do not leave me," she pleaded.

Then Ruth kissed her sister-in-law and stroked her pretty head, saying: "Come with me, Orpah. For three of us the danger will not be so great. Naomi and I will guard thee. Have no fear, sister, and come."

And Orpah, seeing that Ruth was determined, said: "I will come to be near thee, Ruth." And she let Ruth lead her down from the knoll toward the house of Naomi where they three lived together.

Naomi had lit the lamps and was loading her panniered dove-gray donkey, which stood by the door, with food and clothing for the journey and some household utensils. She took parched corn and dried figs and dates and olives, and goat cheese and honey, a jar of oil and a jar of wine, a rush mat to sleep on and a warm shaggy quilt of goat's hair. She took the fine flint knife which Elimelech had made her and the bronze shears he had bought for her of an Egyptian merchant. She took the black stone quern and roller with which she ground her grain, and a mass of raw wool and her spinning whorl whose spindle was polished by many years of use in her tireless hands, for she carried it with her, spinning a long strong thread, wherever she went, sitting or standing, walking or riding. . . .

When Ruth and Orpah appeared, Ruth was leading her milk-white donkey and Orpah her brown one, and Naomi was pleased, thinking that they were going to accompany her a little of the way. But when they, too, began packing —Ruth her bronze forks and silver spoons, and Orpah her boxes of perfumes and ointments—Naomi said to them:

"But are you not staying in this house after I go? I give it to you."

And Ruth said: "We are going with thee to the land of Israel."

"But the men of Moab will not let you go," said Naomi.

"That is what I said also," cried Orpah; and Naomi saw plainly that Orpah was loath to go.

"We will wait until nightfall; they are all up on the hill, and we shall not be seen then," said Ruth.

Then Naomi went to them and said: "Listen to me, my daughters. Return each of you to the house of your mother, and the Lord deal kindly with you as you have dealt with the dead and with me. And the Lord grant you that you may find rest each of you in the house of her husband." Then she kissed them both, and they wept.

But Ruth said again: "We are going with thee to thy people."

And Naomi said: "But you know not whereof you speak. It is a long and dangerous journey to Judah. The desolate country by the dead Salt Sea is infested with wild beasts, with jackals and lions, and the roads with barbarous men. My old bones they may sniff at and pass by, but you, my sweet ones, they will pursue——"

"That is just what I tried to tell her!" cried Orpah, hiding her frightened face against Ruth's shoulder.

But Ruth said: "Against the wild beasts we will build fires; and from the men we will hide, or we will deceive them by smearing our faces with mud. In any event three will be safer than one, and thou and I together can surely safeguard Orpah."

"Say that we can, my daughter. And say that you come in safety to Judah. What will become of you there? Famine made me an exile from my home and death has made me a childless widow in a strange land; and you have seen how it is with me here. In my homeland among my own people my lot will be better; therefore do I return. But there in Judah you will be, each of you, what I have been here—a childless widow among strangers. For I have no other sons there to give you for husbands." Naomi smiled sadly. "And even if I married again, it is not likely —now is it?—that sons would issue from this old womb again. And even if a miracle happened to me as it happened to the wife of Abraham, the first patriarch in Israel —to his Sarah who conceived Isaac when she was ninety— even if I bore two sons now, you would not wait for them to grow to manhood, would you?"

Then Ruth, who dearly loved the wise old woman, spoke to her with the simple forthrightness that was part of her sturdy beauty: "I loved thy son Mahlon and I want no other man now to replace him. But even if I did, and say but for Orpah's sake, surely there are other men in Judah, are there not?"

And Naomi answered proudly: "Indeed, there are other men in Judah. Among the sons of Israel there are many valiant young men who would look not without favor upon two such young women as you. But," and her face fell, "I have to tell you that when Moses had brought the children of Israel up out of the land of Egypt he said to them: *An Ammonite or a Moabite shall not enter into the assembly of the Lord, because they met you not with bread and water on the way when ye came forth out of Egypt, and because they hired Balaam to curse you,* and therefore——"

"Thou seest," said Orpah eagerly, "they are forbidden to marry us!"

"Then why," said Ruth to Orpah, "why did Mahlon

and Chilion marry us? And Mahlon when he wooed me told me how Moses himself, when he had killed an Egyptian slave driver and fled away into Midian, there married Zipporah the daughter of a Midianite priest."

Then Naomi smiled sagely; and she took from the hand of Orpah a silver box she was packing with perfumes; and Naomi polished its cover on her sleeve and held it up before the face of Ruth and the face of Orpah. "See for yourself," she said, "why Mahlon married you, and Chilion Orpah. Men always find good reasons for forgetting their precepts when their desire is great. There are some in Israel who say that that old law of Moses was meant only against the men of Moab and Ammon, not against the women. And my sons, when they set eyes upon you, became of that mind." She returned the box to Orpah. "But most of the children of Israel, I must tell you truly, are not so minded."

"Thou seest!" said Orpah to Ruth. "Even if we come there safely we shall be reviled. Here we are the daughters of princes of the house of King Eglon, and have known poverty and loneliness only since the death of our men. Here we can easily find us husbands again."

Naomi said: "That is true. And would you remain without husbands? No, my daughters, and it grieves me for your selves that the hand of the Lord has been against me."

And they wept again, and Orpah kissed her mother-in-law, and she said: "Alas that in Israel, in the land of left-handed Ehud who killed our King Eglon, we shall be reviled and outcast, we shall only dry out and shrivel up——"

And Ruth said: "But surely they will not revile us when they see that we wish to sojourn with them and become women of Israel."

And Orpah cried: "But I do not want to become one of them, like a stranger!"

But Ruth silenced her gently and then stood at the door listening to the noise of the orgy on the torchlit high place, to the drum-beaten shrieks of drunken ecstasy and deathly agony. . . . "Nevertheless," she said, "we must not stay here."

"Do not leave me, Ruth!" wailed Orpah, torn between her fears and the insidious call of the revelry.

"Then come with us, Orpah," said Ruth, embracing the tormented girl and trying to comfort her.

And Naomi, seeing how they were distraught, said to them: "Come with me, both of you, as far as the River Arnon. By then you will know your minds and can easily return."

So Orpah dried her tears and helped Ruth to load their two donkeys.

Then they put out the lamps, and the three women left the house and mounted their donkeys, the gray, the milk-white and the brown. And they went out of the city which was dark and all but deserted so that they rode unmolested until they came to pass by the hill of the high place upon which the flaring torches of the revelers swarmed about the bloody stones of sacrifice, around the feast before the gods, of kids boiled in their mothers' milk, and among the trees of the grove where they sang and danced naked about a golden calf and the priests taught their obscene orgies.

And the three women, urging their donkeys along the dark road below would have passed there unheeded, were it not that the two princes, the burly twin brothers who had shouted to Ruth and Orpah at the graves, now weary of the wantons on the hill had taken it into their drunken heads to go down and bring those two fresh young women up to the high place. So, naked as they were, they took a torch and went staggering down the hill and came to the road just in time to intercept Naomi, who was riding ahead.

"And where art thou going in the night, old witch?" one brother demanded, the torchlight gleaming in his wild eyes and upon his powerful flesh. "Is it possible thou hast changed heart and art coming up to our revels?"

"No," said Naomi. "I am leaving Moab to return to Israel, my homeland, to Bethlehem in Judah. And that should please you."

"Indeed that pleases us," answered the other. But the first one, having spied Ruth's white donkey in the darkness behind Naomi, said angrily: "But dost thou think we will let thee take our women away from us?" And he went to Ruth's donkey and took hold of its head; and the other one bearing the torch went to Orpah. And this one said to Orpah: "Thou dost not wish to go with her, dost thou, my pigeon," and he drunkenly fondled her. "Thou wouldst stay here, wouldst thou not, and come with us up to the high place and become the fertile wife of one of us." And he drew Orpah's donkey away up the hill, taking the torch with him and calling back to his brother to bring Ruth.

And Orpah, fearful yet fascinated by his wanton love-making and by the excitement of the shouting and the music drifting down from above, cried out: "I cannot go with thee, Naomi. Farewell!" And: "Come thou with us, Ruth!" she called back as her seducer led her up into the swarming torchlit darkness of the grove.

But Ruth remained unmoved. Though inwardly shaken by his naked lust she repulsed with firm hands the befuddled fondling of the other brother. And when she saw that Orpah was gone up the hill she said to him: "I am going with my mother-in-law as far as the River Arnon to see her on her way." And she pushed her donkey past him and went to Naomi and whispered, "Let us hasten away into the darkness; he is too drunken to follow on foot and without a light."

So the two women spurred their donkeys and rode off, leaving him in the road shouting: "Mind thou returnest, Ruth, or we will come after thee!" And then he went staggering up the hill after his brother and Orpah, calling to them: "Wait for me!"

And the two women riding away in the darkness below heard the voice of Orpah crying: "Come back, Ruth, come back!" blown down to them on the wind with the noise of the revelers. But as they continued northward on the King's highway across the wide plain of Moab, riding as fast as their donkeys would go, the sounds of revelry died away in the darkness behind them. . .

Toward dawn they came to where the highway crossed the River Arnon and there they stopped. And Naomi said to Ruth: "Now think well, my daughter, if it would not be better to leave me here and return to your people and their gods."

And Ruth said, "I dearly loved thy son Mahlon who weaned me away from the ways of my people and their gods. And now that Mahlon is gone I have left only thee, his mother, to love."

Naomi kissed her daughter-in-law and she said: "It is a hard journey to Judah; and it is not easy to be a stranger in a strange land. Even though we in Israel have been commanded by Moses to consider the stranger among us, and to treat him justly, still it will not be easy for you there."

Then said Ruth: "Entreat me not to leave thee, and to return from following after thee: For whither thou goest, I will go; and where thou lodgest, I will lodge. Thy people shall be my people, and thy God my God. Where thou diest, there will I die, and there will I be buried: The Lord do so to me, and more also, if aught but death part thee and me."

And when Naomi saw that Ruth was steadfastly minded to go with her she left off speaking, and the two women rode on, Naomi on her dove-gray donkey and Ruth on her milk-white one. And for fear of pursuit by the men of Moab they turned there at the river and left the King's highway. They crossed over the Arnon there at the ford where it was shallow and turned westward following the brawling course of the river as it went plunging down its wild gorge, falling away from the high cool plains of Moab toward the torrid basin of the dead Salt Sea.

As the two donkeys went stepping down the steep ravine, Naomi took out her spinning whorl and her wool and began spinning a long strong thread. And, as they rode downward along the green flowering bank of the river that ran among mossy rocks and rested in cool shining tree-shaded pools, the two women talked, the old and the young, the one garrulously wise and the other eagerly attentive. And much of their talk, as is the way with women, was about the ways of men. Ruth asked many questions and Naomi answered them and counseled her out of the store of her wisdom and her long experience.

"For I must prepare you," she said, "for your life among the men of Judah in Israel." And Naomi, as she rode and talked, steadily turned her spinning whorl; and it was as if, with the long thread she spun, she was spinning out the story not only of her own men—of Elimelech, her husband, and Mahlon and Chilion, her sons—or merely of the men of Israel, but of all mankind since the beginning. . . .

"Now my Elimelech was a fine strong young man when I married him, and a hero in Israel. He was among the first to go up against Gibeah in that dreadful civil war against the Benjamites in which Judah was commanded to go ahead of all Israel; and twenty-two thousand of our men were slain the first day and eighteen thousand the second. And it was my Elimelech who devised the trick to lure the men of Benjamin out of their city on the third day and thus turned the tide of the battle for us. And they made him a judge in Judah; for there are no kings in Israel and every man does that which is right in his own eyes, the Israelites being a stiff-necked people and freedom-loving, remembering their bitter bondage under Pharaoh in Egypt from which Moses led them back to Canaan. So instead of kings they have judges to lead them in battle and to judge between them in their own differences, and the judges are chosen from among their heroes; for men, even stiff-necked men, are inclined to exalt their heroes, though heroes are often far from wise, as witness strong Samson, who——" and there Naomi suddenly bethought herself and stopped talking as her withered hands unraveled a knot in the skein of wool.

"And who was this Samson?" asked Ruth, riding close alongside Naomi. "I dearly love to hear tales of strong and heroic men."

But Naomi said no more of Samson. "My Elimelech," she continued, "was both heroic and wise, a strong and a thoughtful man, such as are to be found more often among the Israelites than among the other peoples who prize strength alone and not thoughtfulness."

"I remember," said Ruth, "how my father belittled Mahlon not only for his frailty but because he was thoughtful. And were it not for the high price he paid for me my father would not have considered giving me to Mahlon, though it was his very thoughtfulness, the like of which was unknown to me among the men of Moab, that drew me to Mahlon. And my father was wont to say that all Israelites thought too much. They are too shrewd, he would say."

"The strong mistrust the thoughtful," said Naomi, nodding her head as she spun the whorl, "often, to be sure, with very good reason—as the father of all Israel, shrewd Jacob, proved long ago to Esau his powerful brother, whom he tricked out of his inheritance. But my Elimelech, who was both thoughtful and strong, did not lack the foolish pride of strong men. And when the land of Israel was afflicted by a great famine although the Lord God of Israel had promised us a land flowing with milk and honey, the people, who relied on the wisdom of those heroes and judges who had always risen to save them, came to Elimelech for guidance out of their calamity; and my Elimelech, seeing that he had failed them and remembering how Joseph in Egypt had wisely laid up a store of food in the years of plenty for the years of famine—proud Elimelech, whose mother had well named him 'kingly'— could not face his suffering people nor bear their reproaches, although it was doubtless because of their own backsliding that this calamity had come upon them. So he left the land of Israel and went to Moab; and there he proved our old proverb which says:

Pride goeth before destruction
And a haughty spirit before a fall."

And Ruth saw bitter tears rise to the eyes of Naomi as she spun her whorl faster; and bitterness was on her thin wrinkled lips as the old woman continued speaking: "And had I known then what time has since taught me about the stubborn ways of men and the power women have over them, I would have used guile, as the mothers of Israel did when they had to: I would even have deceived my Elimelech, as our mother Rebekah deceived her husband Isaac into giving the blessing to smooth gentle Jacob instead of his wild hairy brother Esau, and as our mother Rachel deceived her own father Laban when she hid his gods and saved her beloved husband Jacob from his anger. I would have prevented Elimelech and my sons from going to Moab."

"But then," said Ruth, "I should never have known thee and thy ways, Naomi, nor thy son Mahlon, and I should still be a foolish young woman in Moab, sunk in its abominations."

And Naomi looked up from her spinning into the dark eyes of her loyal young daughter-in-law and leaned over to her and kissed her.

"Not that I do not think I have much yet to learn," said Ruth, as their donkeys, the dove-gray and the milk-white one together, went stepping daintily down the deepening and widening gorge of the river whose banks were blue with wild iris. "Especially," said Ruth, "of the ways of men."

Naomi said: "In Israel we have a saying:

> *There be three things too wonderful for me:*
> *Yea, four that I know not:*
> *The way of an eagle in the air;*
> *The way of a serpent upon a rock;*
> *The way of a ship in the midst of the sea;*
> *And the way of a man with a maid."*

And Naomi glanced keenly at Ruth; and then, resuming her spinning, she said: "Indeed you have much yet to learn, my daughter. For you are still young and you were but a child when you married my first-born son whom I named Mahlon because he was so frail, so pale and puling, so sickly even in infancy."

"And you, too, like Rebekah," said Ruth, "you loved Mahlon the frail one better than Chilion the robust one."

"That is so," said Naomi. "And yet when I see how often it happens that the first-born are weaklings it seems not entirely without reason that the thoughtless peoples who worship strength are wont to sacrifice their first-born before their gods. For frail children are apt to grow up into weak and troubled men, too gentle for the struggle of life and too troubled by their own thoughtfulness which wins them the enmity of the strong. And perhaps that is why Jacob, the father of all Israel, on his deathbed in Egypt insisted on giving his first blessing not to the elder but to the younger of Joseph's two sons."

"And was Jacob himself the first-born son of his father?" asked Ruth.

"Well," said Naomi hesitantly, "Jacob and Esau were twins—though it is said that Esau came forth first and Jacob had hold of his brother's heel, which would make him the younger, and he should not have been the weaker —but they were really twins and the rule therefore does not apply to them. But why the first-born should be the weaker of two sons of the same father I cannot tell you, my daughter, only that it is more often so. With my Elimelech who was both strong and thoughtful it was as if he had divided the powers of his flesh and spirit between his two sons. Mahlon, the first-born, got his wise spirit, and Chilion, the second, got his lusty flesh. So much so that while delicate Mahlon reviled the abominations of Moab his hardier brother Chilion was drawn to them."

"And was it for that reason," asked Ruth, "that, when your sons married, Mahlon chose me and Chilion took Orpah?"

Naomi smiled as she spun. "Now that would be difficult to say, my daughter. You were both very young, you and Orpah, so young that you had not yet been taken up to the rites of spring. Yet even then as a maiden you were gentler, more earnest in spirit than Orpah, and it is possible that Mahlon preferred that in you. But there is no denying that men have a power over women too. So it may well be that—because gentle, thoughtful Mahlon, who feared the violence of the men of Moab and despised their thoughtlessness, married you, while Orpah was taken by lusty Chilion who, despite the teaching of his father and the laws of his forefathers, went up to the high place—that now you are here with me and Orpah remained there in the City of Moab." And Naomi glanced again from her spinning into the dark eyes of Ruth. "Now tell me truly, my daughter, were not you, too, tempted at times by the fierce lustful ways of those princes of Moab?"

And Ruth said: "I cannot deny that the sight of their manly strength sometimes moved me in a way gentle Mahlon never did—so that my flesh fainted in the presence of their lust; but I——" And she stopped speaking.

"But," said Naomi, "even in the little time you lived with my gentle Mahlon you had learned from him what Moses knew and taught the children of Israel—that, untamed in man, his joyous life-giving lust turns to a dreadful death-dealing thing—which Mahlon saw when his brother Chilion died of the foul disease he had got on the high place." She mused sadly a moment over her spinning. "My Elimelech used to say, *From the forest itself comes the handle of the axe that fells it,* meaning that men have in their hearts the seeds of their own destruction. And man cannot be a mere animal: he is either better than the beast, or he is worse. All the same it is a pity my poor Mahlon had not got a little of his brother's robust lustiness, then he would have been like his father, both wise and strong, and he would have lived to make you as good a husband as Elimelech made me—for all his foolish pride." And Naomi sighed fondly and smiled as she spun. "And is it not curious, my daughter, that a woman can yet love her husband and her sons though she sees plainly all their faults; while it seems that a man, to love a woman, must see no fault in her." And she raised her quavering voice again and sang:

> *Lo thou art all fair, my love;*
> *And there is no blemish in thee.*

"Thus sing the men of Israel. And it is his vision of her, not the real woman, that a man loves. And perhaps that is why, when a good man loves a woman, he has the power to make her a better woman. But however good a man may be he must above all be manly to make a full and happy woman of the maiden he marries. And my frail, thoughtful Mahlon was good but not manly—not much of a mate for you." And her wise old eyes looked again into the dark troubled young ones beside her. "Yes, my daughter, I have known; though Elimelech used to say:

> *The heart knows its own bitterness;*
> *And even with its joy no other can meddle.*"

Ruth said: "It is strange that among the men of Moab I never saw one with the spirit of Mahlon, whom I greatly loved despite his frailty."

And Naomi said: "Perhaps it is because the Moabites sacrifice their first-born sons that there is not to be found among them such men, gentle, thoughtful and frail as my Mahlon was. But look there, the Salt Sea!" cried Naomi, pointing downward.

For as they descended with the River Arnon it had turned to a steaming stream rushing down a hot gulley of stones, naked but for prickly cactus and thorn; and there at the foot of the rocky ravine the river fell into the dead Salt Sea, lying like molten metal under the sun that hung blood red over a maze of mountains on the farther shore.

And then, looking out on that desolate expanse, Naomi told Ruth the old tale of Lot's wife who, because she looked back at Sodom and Gemorrah, was turned to a pillar of salt. It was there, and Naomi pointed southward, at the foot of that very sea which was salt to this day, the old wives in Israel said, because a woman had looked back behind her. "And however that may be," said Naomi to Ruth with her wise old smile, "you, my daughter, must put your life in Moab behind you now, and look back no more."

And Ruth smiled too, though her young heart was heavy with anxiety for the future and longing for the peaceful past with gentle Mahlon, as they turned their sweating donkeys and went northward along the arid shore of the sea. Its leaden waters hardly rippled beneath the hot heavy wind which blew at sunset over that silent uninhabited place of evil-smelling sand, bare burnt hills, and beetling cliffs.

And when the sun sank behind the mountains they stopped by a brook running into the sea and washed and made them a meal of bread and cheese and dried figs; and they gathered dry thorn bushes and made a ring of fire around their resting place to keep away the howling jackals and the yelping foxes which they heard all the night in their fitful sleep. Once Naomi woke Ruth and pointed with trembling fingers to the shining eyes of some wild beast glaring at them from the darkness beyond the dying fire. And Ruth overcame her own fears and rose up and replenished the fire and fashioned a sling and beat off the beast with stones she slung at it. And she took Naomi in her arms and comforted the terrified old woman until she slept again. . . .

The next day they continued northward along the seashore. And riding her dove-gray donkey in the bright warm daylight Naomi was again of good cheer and resumed her spinning and her talk, laughing at her fears of the night before. . . . "And men like to think," she said, "that we are all and always like that, fearful creatures, dependent on them for our safety. Even my Elimelech who was so strong seemed troubled sometimes by any sign of a strength of spirit I might have learned from him; and he seemed happiest when he was comforting me in my foolish fearfulness as you did last night, my daughter. But you who might have learned timidity from poor Mahlon, are as courageous as those women of valor whom the men of Israel celebrate in a song I shall teach you some day. For though, like most men, the Israelites do not appear to want their own wives to be strong, still do they cherish the memories of those determined mothers in Israel, like Abraham's Sarah and Isaac's Rebekah and Jacob's Rachel and of prophetesses like Miriam the sister of Moses and Zipporah the Midianitess, his wife, who circumcised her own son and saved the life of Moses from the wrath of God. And the men of Israel even sing the praises of valiant women who have won battles for them."

"And was Jael, of whom thou didst speak to the reveler

24

was she who killed Sisera one of these?" asked Ruth, and her dark eyes shone with new fire which the words of Naomi had kindled, for Ruth had a vision of becoming herself a renowned woman in Israel.

"Yes, Jael, though she was not one of their own women but the wife of a Kenite," said Naomi, ceasing her spinning and proudly raising her head. "And Deborah, too—Deborah the great woman of God!"

"Tell me of them," begged Ruth," of the valiant women in Israel."

And Naomi said: "When the Israelites, softened in the sixty years since Moses left them and weakened by their backsliding to Baal worship, feared to come forth and fight the gathering hosts of King Jabin of Canaan and his general, Sisera, in the north country, it was valiant Deborah who roused the men of Israel to battle. Princes and shepherds came to her call out of all the tribes. And Deborah called upon the Lord God of Israel for help and he, too, heard her call and it is said that the stars in their courses fought against Sisera and the River Kishon rose up and swept his fallen army away and Sisera fled and sought refuge in the tent of Heber the Kenite."

"But what of Jael?" asked Ruth. "Tell me what Jael did."

"Jael was the wife of Heber, one of the Kenites who were friendly to Israel. And it is told in our Book of Remembrance that she went out to meet Sisera and said to him, *Turn in, my lord, turn in and fear not.* And he went into the tent and lay down and she covered him with a rug. And he said to her, *Give me, I pray thee, a little water to drink; for I am thirsty.* And she opened a skin of milk and gave him to drink. And he said to her, *Stand in the door of the tent and it shall be when any man doth come and inquire of thee and say, Is there any man here? that thou shalt say, No.* Then Jael took a tent pin and she took a hammer in her hand and went softly to him and smote the pin into his temples, and it pierced through into the ground."

Then, seeing the look of horror in the eyes of Ruth, Naomi said: "I tell this to you who are going to be a woman in Israel only to prove that though in the land of Israel as in other lands men are wont to think of women as weak and unreliable, changing in spirit with their time of the month and their years, yet have women in Israel shown themselves firm and strong as any man, sometimes when need be even more determined than their men. And to this day the men of Israel sing of Jael, who like yourself, Ruth, was not one of their women;" and she raised up her old voice and sang:

> *Blessed above women shall Jael be,*
> > *Blessed shall she be above women in the tent!*
> *He asked for water, and she gave him milk;*
> > *She brought him butter in a lordly dish.*
> *She put her hand to the nail,*
> > *And her right hand to the workman's hammer;*
> *And with the hammer she smote Sisera.*
> *She smote through his head,*
> > *Yea, she pierced and struck through his temples.*
> *At her feet he bowed, he fell, he lay:*
> *At her feet he bowed, he fell:*
> > *Where he bowed, there he fell down dead."*

And Naomi said: "Now sing it with me."

Then Ruth's young voice joined with Naomi's as she began again:

> *Blessed above women shall Jael be. . .*

26

and the two women sang together, the elder teaching the younger, their voices ringing bravely against the forbidding rocks as they rode northward skirting the rim of the dead and silent sea.

Late that afternoon the narrow track they followed climbed to a shelf on a cliff overhanging the sea, and toward evening the hungry donkeys, picking their way among heaps of rubble in which lay shards of old pottery, stopped to crop the sparse grass springing up on a hillock surmounted by crumbling walls. And there was a well of water and a pair of palm trees; so the two women camped there for the night.

"This is the ruins of an ancient fortified city," said Naomi, preparing a place under the palms for their meal while Ruth laid the fires. "Doubtless the men of Reuben took it from the men of Sihon who dwelt here before the Israelites returned from bondage in Egypt. And this is also odd about the men of Israel: that they are by nature lovers of peace, greeting each other with 'Peace unto you' and 'Unto you peace' so that their more violent and less thoughtful neighbors are wont to consider them slavishly fearful of might. And yet given a just cause and aroused to anger they can be as violent and ruthless as their enemies, though *Thou shalt not murder* is one of the ten commandments which Moses brought them down from Mount Sinai. Thus you will find the men of Israel curiously divided in spirit and often tormented within themselves, especially those who, like my Elimelech, are both strong and thoughtful. The spirit of that Moabite prince who took Orpah up to the high place was not so divided. Like any animal he lives for the satisfaction of his untamed appetites. He is not troubled about his violence and his lust and he would no more think of restraining them than

27

would a wild tiger. Nor do his gods, which are lovers of violence and lust, command him to be otherwise."

"Yet, on the other hand," said Ruth as they sat and ate, "it never seemed to me that my Mahlon was divided in spirit. Though he was troubled by the abominations of Moab and the frailty of his own flesh, a more peaceable man never lived, always gentle and self-restrained."

Naomi said: "You must not judge all the men of Israel by poor Mahlon. It is easy enough for a frail man to be virtuous. If you had lived with a man like my Elimelech you would know what I mean. But you will see for yourself when you come in to Judah. And now let us lie down and rest. For I am weary as if I had been wandering forty years in the wilderness like Moses toward the promised land. Tomorrow if all goes well we should reach the River Jordan."

So they laid them down to sleep in the circle of fires Ruth had made; but Naomi roused Ruth again to say that there was not one but a host of yellow-eyed beasts moving all about them, until Ruth showed her that it was but a flock of fireflies rising in the darkness and the rustling of the palm fronds in the night breeze.

And all the next day they followed the narrow track northward along the cliffs above the edge of the silent sea, but because Naomi's donkey, that dove-gray creature with deceptive liquid eyes, got balky as Balaam's ass and would not go on without being beaten, they did not reach Jordan by sunset and had to make camp again by the way, within sight of a high mountain peak rising up from the plain to the east.

And Ruth said as they lay down to rest: "That is Mount Peor, is it not? I have heard my father tell of it with awe; for it is the home of his gods—Baal-Peor and his wife Ashtar. And I have heard him speak of it in anger, too, as the place where Balaam was brought by our King Balak to curse the Israelites but was moved instead to bless them."

And Naomi said: "It is often so between the Israelites and their enemies who are torn between hate and envy of this peculiar people of whom Balaam said, looking down on them from that mountain:

> *Lo, it is a people that dwell alone,*
> *And shall not be reckoned among the nations.*

But to the children of Israel that is not Mount Peor but Mount Nebo where weary Moses after patiently leading the children of Israel through the desert went up to look out on the land the Lord God of Israel had promised them, but which the Lord had told Moses he would not enter with them."

"And why," asked Ruth, "was Moses denied entry into the promised land after leading his people all that long way through the wilderness? I, who have come only from Moab and now look forward so eagerly to our arrival in Judah, can easily imagine how his heart must have grieved him as Moses stood there on Mount Nebo. Why then did the Lord forbid him to go into the land?"

Naomi said: "Long before, when they had come into the wilderness of Zin where there was no water, the children of Israel cried out against Moses and Aaron, saying, *Wherefore have ye made us to come up out of Egypt, to bring us into this evil place?* And the Lord gave Moses a rod and instructed him to speak to a rock in the name of the Lord and it would give forth water. But Moses in his impatience did not speak to the rock as the Lord had told him; he smote the rock with his rod, twice. And though the water came forth abundantly and the congregation drank, and their cattle, too, yet the Lord said to Moses and Aaron, *Ye shall not bring this assembly into the land which I have given them.*"

And Ruth, lying beside Naomi, said: "But why did the Lord give Moses the rod if he did not wish him to strike the rock, only to speak to it? Is it not strange that God gives a man the means to do wrong and then punishes him for not doing right?"

Naomi said: "Now that is a question which has troubled man since the very beginning when the Lord God of Israel set the tree of the knowledge of good and evil in the Garden of Eden and told Adam and Eve not to eat of it under pain of death. For the Almighty One does not prevent us from doing evil; he lets us have the power to do both good and evil and bids us learn and heed his laws and choose between good and evil. So he gave Moses the rod with which he might strike though he bid him speak to the rock."

"But surely," said Ruth, "the impatience of Moses on that occasion was forgiveable."

"To anyone but the Lord God of Israel," said Naomi. "For the God of Israel, though he is jealous of all other gods and wrathfully chastises his people for their back-sliding to Baal worship, demands of his people that each one curb his spirit, submitting faithfully to the instruction of the Almighty One. So Moses, who had in his impatience displayed his own power instead of the power of the word of God, was punished by being kept out of the promised land, the land flowing with milk and honey that he could see plainly from Nebo; and there he died alone, and no one knows where he was buried."

And Ruth said: "Would that Moses were still alive; for surely he, who thought to teach the Israelites forbearance for the stranger while they were yet wandering in the wilderness, would have befriended me—for all that he said a Moabite shall not enter into the congregation of Israel." And she looked up at the mountain whose summit under the darkling sky shone blood red in the last light of the setting sun.

And Naomi said: "Some say he was murdered and his body hidden away by those who hated him for the hardship they had suffered in the flight from Egypt and wished he had left them there in bondage instead of bringing them out to serve this jealous God, who is one God yet is everywhere and commands them to such self-restraint as most men can hardly practice. And others say that the grave of Moses was hidden lest it become a shrine where his fellow men whom he had brought to freedom might come and bow down and worship him; and that would be abominable to their jealous God who differs from the gods of other men in that he is singular where they are many and while they are capricious he is lawful—not to be swayed or placated by cruel sacrifices, or celebrated in lewd and beastly rites, but served in learning and obeying his commandments which are the laws of all creation and of life. And it is this search for God's will under leaders like Moses who was concerned not merely with the acts of men but with their desires and their thoughts, it is this that has troubled the spirits of the strong and thoughtful men of Israel. They are torn between the promptings of their flesh and the commandments of their austere God who is the Lord of all creation yet himself has no wife. But a true man needs both. For without his lusty body he is no man and without that knowledge of God he is no more than the brute beast. But the man who has both, I can tell you, is not easy for a woman to live with. Just as he spends a good part of his life learning the laws of God, you must spend a good part of your life learning his laws. And sometimes it seems easier for a woman to learn the laws of God than of a man. Consider even Moses, the greatest of them, of whom it is said: *The man Moses was very meek, above all the men which were upon the Earth;* yet he killed an Egyptian who was smiting a Hebrew slave; and in his impatience he smote the rock for water, as I have just told you; and again in his anger at sight of the Israelites worshiping a golden calf he broke the tablets of the law which he brought down from Sinai. But only with knowledge can we avoid or overcome difficulties and reap rewards in living with such men. And when you know such a man, my daughter, you will surely love him, as I loved my Elimelech. So despite all I have borne and suffered yet do I counsel you to find such a man in Judah and marry him. For our Mahlon is gone forever, and what the Lord God said to Adam: *It is not good that the man should be alone,* is it not equally true of woman?" said Naomi to Ruth.

But to this Ruth made no reply, for she was fast asleep. So Naomi leaned over and kissed her gently, and she covered her well with the warm shaggy quilt of goat's hair and lay down to sleep beside her. . . .

In the morning they went westward again, rounding the northern end of the Salt Sea and approaching the ford of Jordan, which there falls into the sea. And there they came again within sight of the King's highway and they saw far distant a caravan coming: a band of Moabite marauders returning from a raid in the land of Israel, their swift camels laden with the booty they had seized. And seeing what looked like two women on donkeys in the distance two men moved from the course of the caravan and rode toward them.

And fortunate it was that there were cavernous rocks nearby, and Naomi made Ruth go quickly into hiding among them with her white donkey. And Naomi took the sharp flint knife Elimelech had made her and she gave it to Ruth, saying, "I have no need of this; me they will not molest." And Ruth took the knife and hid it in her sleeve as she waited within a cave.

And the old woman was apparently alone, struggling with her obstinate donkey when the two Moabites on their camels drew up beside her. And they were the two burly brothers, the twin princes of the City of Moab. They were young and strong but not handsome. Their bushy black eyebrows met over their noses, and their nostrils were thick and flat like those of their long-necked mounts and they had also the strong smell of their camels.

"What did I tell thee?" said one. "It is the old witch, Naomi. And where is our Ruth?" he demanded, looking around for her.

"I prevailed upon her to return two days ago," said Naomi. "And I am alone with this cursed creature, this son of Belial that thinks he is Balaam's ass and has seen the Angel of the Lord!" and she spat into the face of the donkey, loudly calling down maledictions upon its ancestry.

"Thou art lying," said the Moabite, "for we would have met Ruth upon the highway when we set forth on this raid."

"And I would have sworn by Peor and Ashtar," insisted the other, "that I saw from the distance a young woman with you, a pretty one."

"But that," said Naomi, "was only the mirage of your

33

male desire. I have known in my time what that is like."

"Is it possible!" he said, as if in amazement.

"It was possible," said Naomi returning his stare. "Men are so greedy! At any age! You have no idea how peaceful it is to be an old and unbeautiful woman, no longer sought after and hunted, as unmolested as a sun-bleached bone lying in the sand."

Then the two young men could not help laughing at her sally, but they kept looking around for some sign of Ruth, who stood very still with her donkey concealed in the cave not a stone's throw away.

And Ruth from her hiding place looked upon the two men and knew that if they discovered her there she would take her own life rather than return with them to the City of Moab. For she knew that she had been weaned forever from the bestial ways of the men of Moab and she could never abide them nor the slavish ways of their women. So she stood waiting within the cave with the sharp flint knife in her hand, ready, if one of them came upon her, to strike him down, fearlessly, as Jael struck down Sisera.

She heard old Naomi saying: "We did not come by the highway. We came by the shore of the Salt Sea. And if you go back that way you will overtake Ruth. That is if no other man has yet come upon her." And unflinching the old woman returned the gaze of the twin brothers until one of them suddenly leaned down from his camel and kissed her withered cheek saying, "That is for sending her back." Then he wheeled his camel, and the two rode off, laughing aloud, to rejoin their band which then turned and went south by the seashore.

And when they were out of sight Ruth came from her hiding place, laughing too at Naomi who stood rubbing her wrinkled face.

"A man in heat will kiss anything!" the old woman muttered, though she seemed not entirely displeased as she said it. Then she looked up at the sky.

With a rising wind the heavens had darkened to the color of the earth for a sandstorm was blowing in from the desert, and Naomi, being weary and fearful of the river crossing, said: "Let us wait until after the storm." But Ruth, more fearful now of Moabite men than of storms, pleaded that they hasten to cross the Jordan before another caravan came. Once over in Judah among the Israelites they would be safer, she thought.

They arrived at the ford in a dark gale; the wind-driven sand stung their faces; and the river was swollen with the waters of spring. Wild buffalo wallowed in the flooded banks among the rattling reeds of papyrus. But another caravan had appeared on the highway and they determined to cross over at once.

So they urged their donkeys into the turbulent stream, Ruth ahead and leading Naomi's reluctant donkey. And the swift mud-laden water washed over their feet; but they pressed on and had got safely to midstream when Naomi's gray beast, as if remembering her recent mistreatment, balked and stopped.

"Dear donkey, sweet donkey!" pleaded the old woman, as the water rose riffling around her knees. "I did not mean to spit upon you. It was only to fool those stupid men. . . ." But the devilish donkey stood still and shook himself hard, until Naomi slipped from his back into the swirling brown water and would have been swept away had not Ruth come to her rescue and lifted her up again on the donkey's back and beat the beast into carrying her over to the shore.

Then, more dead than alive, Naomi lay in the shelter of a tree while the storm passed and Ruth gathered wood for a fire. And when the old woman was rested and revived she gave fervent thanks to the Lord God of Israel for bringing them safely into the land of Judah, though she remarked to Ruth a bit plaintively that the Lord had not seen fit to do for two women what he had done for Joshua and the priests bearing the ark of the covenant when they came to pass over Jordan on their way to Jericho—for them he had stopped the river which was then also swollen. "And come to think of it," said Naomi, "that was just about this time of year no more than a hundred years ago—but the Lord God of Israel has not been as generous with his miracles to women as to men. He did indeed bring Sarah to child-bed with Isaac when she was ninety years old; but she had provoked him to it by laughing at the possibility until he said, *Is anything too hard for the Lord?* That was a rare case. And perhaps it is because the Lord rarely performs miracles for women that we are prone to take things in our own hands. For the Lord God of Israel is certainly a man's god; and the land of Israel like the rest of this world is a man's world."

Nevertheless, as they dried their drenched and muddy garments by the fire she gave praise again to the men of Judah, saying how much better they treated their women than did the men of Ammon and Moab, who looked to women only for the satisfaction of their lust. "Not that the men of Judah are not lusty," she hastened to assure Ruth, as she spread out her sodden wool to dry before the fire. "Indeed I do not mean you to think they are entirely unlike other men. As Moses said: *All men are brothers.* But there are differences in brothers; consider Cain and Abel; Jacob and Esau. And was not the father of Moab the son of the eldest daughter of Lot who was a brother to Abraham—which makes Moab and Israel kin; and I have known Israelites as uncouth as the rudest Moabite. I mean merely to say that the men of Israel are different in that they extol and respect the women they have loved, even when they are old—as witness the story of Abraham and old Sarah in the matter of her son Isaac against Hagar's Ishmael; they are not like the men of other nations who have no regard for women when they no longer serve their lust. And the men of Israel," said Naomi, "though lusty are not given to orgies of lewdness, because their God has forbid them adultery and all the abominations of Ammon and Moab. The Lord God of Israel is not a lover of lust but a lover of love, which is not merely of the flesh but of the spirit. Other nations learn only to fear their gods. The Israelites are taught: *And thou shalt love the Lord thy God with all thy heart, with all thy soul, and with all thy might.* And he has commanded them to honor not only their fathers but their mothers. And it is said that when Moses brought down God's commandments from Sinai and the men were loath to accept them, Moses taught them first to the women, because women are more sensible and because women teach their children and because women can beguile men into doing not only what is evil but what is good. Hence the men of Israel cherish their women and their children, and women and children have played a great part in the history of Israel, even though it is the men who have written that history." And having dried out some wool she began spinning again. "The very name of our great Moses means child, and were it not for two women—his mother who saved him alive despite Pharaoh's edict that all male Israelite children be slain, and the daughter of Pharaoh who rescued him from the bulrushes where his mother had hid him—were it not for those two women, that child would not have lived to lead Israel out of bondage and bring them the laws of the Lord our God. And never would the Israelites sacrifice a child—since the time of Abraham to whom the Lord God appeared to prevent the sacrifice of his beloved son Isaac, bringing him a scapegoat instead." She glanced into Ruth's dark eyes. "You have wanted a child, have you not, my daughter?"

Ruth said: "During my marriage to Mahlon I was torn between my deep desire for a child and my dread that should I bear a daughter she would grow up to take part in the beastly rites of Peor and Ashtar, and should I bear a son he would surely be sacrificed to cruel Chemosh. And so great was my dread that though there were times when I longed for a lustier Mahlon there were also times, especially in the spring, when I was grateful that he lacked the vigor to give me a child. But now tell me this, Naomi: if it is indeed true that first-born sons are apt to be frail children and troubled men why did the Lord God not let Abraham sacrifice Isaac?"

And Naomi said: "We are told in our Book of Remembrance that God wished to prove Abraham, and he bid him take his beloved son Isaac up on Mount Moriah there to sacrifice him. And we are told how Abraham went to do God's bidding and took his son Isaac and two of his young men to accompany him. And we are told that Abraham left the two young men at the foot of the mountain and took the fire and the knife and went up alone with his small son. But we have only the word of Abraham that God, having proved him, then prevented him from making the sacrifice and provided the scapegoat. Now, I am but a woman and I do not mean to deny the story of Abraham, that great forefather of Israel. But men have their own way of telling a story; and that this man Abraham was very shrewd, even before his God, may be seen in the matter of his having beat God down from fifty to ten as the least number of virtuous men for whose sake the evil city of Sodom might be spared. So I venture to say that Abraham who had not feared to teach his God mercy would want to teach his fellow man mercy. And that, it seems to me, is what he was doing on Mount Moriah. What Abraham meant by that story about the scapegoat is that the Lord though fierce in his just anger is yet a god of mercy, the life-giving father of all mankind, his children, loving the weak no less than the strong and wanting no cruel sacrifice of the frailest of them. And this he had already made clear before Isaac was born when he ordered Abraham to circumcise himself and all the males of his tribe, including his son Ishmael—commanding that that small bit of their flesh be taken from every male child born thereafter as a covenant with the Lord in lieu of a human sacrifice, which is done among all the children of Israel to this day. But to return to Isaac of whom you inquired: As it turned out, however, Isaac grew up into no great figure of a man, the least of the forefathers of Israel. He was too much attached to his mother, for whose death he grieved until his father got him a wife Rebekah to take her place; and I sometimes think it may be that our first-born sons are apt to be weaklings because we coddle them more than the others. Certainly Isaac was not like his father Abraham who was both shrewd and strong."

"And was Abraham himself the second son of his father?" asked Ruth.

Naomi stopped her spinning to cast her eyes upward in thought, counting on her gnarled fingers until she said, uncomfortably: "No, he was not. Abraham was the first-born son of Terah. But," and she hastily took up her spinning again, "that proves nothing. I am not like the men:

I do not say that what has often been so, must always be so. Even God Almighty has been known more than once to break his laws for the sake of his children—at least for the men. Not only did he part the Jordan for Joshua as he had parted the Red Sea for Moses, but he stopped the setting sun and the rising moon for Joshua at the battle of Jericho. No, Abraham was a first-born son and he was strong, but he was exceptional," said Naomi firmly.

"But was not Isaac really the second son of Abraham?" asked Ruth, whose eager inquiry was not to be stopped by the sharp glance Naomi gave her: "For didst thou not say that Abraham had had another son by Hagar before Sarah bore Isaac?"

"Yes, Ishmael," said Naomi, impatiently. "But he had been sent away; he did not count, because Isaac was Abraham's first-born by Sarah. And Isaac was certainly a weakling for, when he went to Gerar and opened his father's wells which the Philistines had filled up, he could not contend with the herdsmen of Gerar but moved off before them from one well to another. And then he became blind, and then was deceived by his wife Rebekah into giving Jacob the blessing instead of Esau, all of which proves what I say—well, at least that Isaac was a weakling. Yet out of his weakness came a great good, came Jacob—because of that weakness Jacob became the father of all Israel!"

"And because of the weakness of Mahlon," said Ruth gravely, "I was weaned away from the abominations of Moab and have turned my face, my heart and my soul, to Israel."

"True," said Naomi. "And while the other gods, like cruel Chemosh, say: Sacrifice the weak, for only the strong should survive, the Lord God of Israel says: Save the weak and help them survive, and let all men, weak and strong, learn the laws of God by which they may live. For out of the gentle thoughtfulness of the weak can come great goodness. In Israel it is the custom to dedicate first-born sons to the service of the Lord, for the Lord said to Moses: *The first born of thy sons shalt thou give to me*—not to be slaughtered in sacrifice but to learn his commandments which are for life; and Mahlon had been well taught by his father. And who knows but that because of the spirit of frail Mahlon which turned you from Moab there may yet come from your womb strong sons in Israel, and from them sons who will be very great in Israel."

But Ruth said: "I have still no wish for another man than Mahlon."

"Then tell me, my daughter," said Naomi, looking at the golden amulets on Ruth's brow, each bearing the naked, full-breasted figure of Ashtar, "tell me now, why do you still wear those Moabite charms?"

And Ruth was silent as she looked away for a moment from those keen old eyes. Then she returned their questioning gaze and said: "When I knew that Mahlon could give me no child I went to my mother. And she got from the priest and gave me the amulets to rouse up the passion of Mahlon, for in Moab these golden charms, which only the daughters of princes may wear, were said to have potent magic with men. And my mother bid me also to go up to the spring rites which would make me fertile. And though I was then sorely tempted I did not go up to the high place because Mahlon forbid it me, saying that in the eyes of the Lord God of Israel, the one Almighty God, those rites were abominable. He also said that there was no virtue in such things as amulets, and he let me wear these in order to prove it. And alas it was indeed so, for nothing came of my wearing them. But one day when I had ceased wearing them, Mahlon said that they brought out the beauty of my brow, so I wore them thereafter to please him and I have continued to wear them because they remind me of Mahlon and how he would chant, *Lo, thou art beautiful, my beloved,* when I put them on before him."

And Naomi said sadly: "A woman has need of children," looking upon the swift river where it ran out into the desolate Salt Sea. "Lacking a child to love, the heart of a woman, though she may get much love from men, must grow bitter in time—just as that sea, lacking an outlet, remains bitter though all the sweet water of Jordan pours endlessly into it."

"Thou art very wise, Naomi," said Ruth, her dark eyes filled with longing.

And Naomi said: "I sorely wish that you had a son. I would teach him all I have learned from life; and he would teach his sons and they would be wise men in Israel and they would write down my wisdom in books and my life would not be lost in the death of my sons but would be redeemed, and the name of Elimelech and of Mahlon would be preserved upon the earth."

Ruth said: "And wouldst thou teach my child all those laws of the Lord God of Israel?"

And Naomi said: "Indeed I would, as Moses instructed us saying: *And these words which I command thee this day shall be upon thine heart and thou shalt teach them diligently unto thy children.* But why do you ask this?"

And Ruth said: "This seems no child's God, this Lord of unchanging laws, who is not to be swayed like the gods of Moab by the wishes and gifts of his children."

Naomi smiled then and said: "For the fulfillment of all

his wishes your child would have us. And what joy it would be for me to hold him in my arms and take him into my bosom, and be nurse to him and sing him sweet songs:

For lo, the winter is past,"

Naomi sang softly in her quavering old voice, swaying back and forth as she sang:

The rain is over and gone.

And Ruth, too, took up the song in her sweet voice:

The flowers appear on the earth,

rocking over her empty arms as she sang;

The time of the singing of birds is come
And the voice of the turtle is heard in our land. . . .

And both women, the old and the young, as their song died away sat looking with wistful delight into the dying fire, until Naomi roused herself saying: "But sitting down here by Jordan will not get you with child, my daughter. Come now, let us be on our way up to Bethlehem and see if there is yet a good man for you in Judah."

And Ruth rose up saying: "But even if I wished for another husband, say, for the sake of a child—what Israelite in his own land among his own women would look with favor upon me—a woman of Moab?"

Naomi, smiling sagely, looked at Ruth in her worn and bedraggled garments and said: "It would help matters if you were better clothed; but even the most austere man of Judah cannot fail to see your beauty, and the Lord God of Israel, who has instructed his children to be fruitful and multiply, will surely provide for you." And then suddenly bethinking herself Naomi said: "But to be sure, living so long in Moab I had forgotten our levirate law!"

"And what is that?" asked Ruth.

"That it is the right," said Naomi, "and indeed the duty of the brother-in-law of a childless widow to marry her and give her a son to inherit and redeem the land of the dead and preserve his name upon it. And where there is no brother-in-law, the nearest kinsman has the right. Now I am naturally too old to beget an heir to the land Elimelech left in Judah; but you, my daughter, shall do that!" said Naomi eagerly. "And you shall preserve the name of Mahlon upon it! I know not who remains of the family of Elimelech in Bethlehem, but we shall see when we get there!"

But Ruth shook her head and said: "Much as a son would delight me, and thee too, Naomi—and much as I would wish to preserve the name of Mahlon upon his inheritance—dost thou think I would want any other man for the father of my son than Mahlon whom I dearly loved? And dost thou think I would have happiness married to a man who did so because of a law?"

Naomi shrugged her thin shoulders and smiling patiently said: "We shall see, we shall see. Come now; let us go on up into Judah."

So they continued westward. And the next day at sunrise they left the valley of Jordan and urged their donkeys, the dove-gray and the milk-white one, up the rugged hills of Judah, the hills of the ancient homeland which the children of Israel had terraced with stone walls and turned with loving labor into a fertile and fruitful garden. There were snowy-blossoming orchards of pear and plum and the lilac clouds of almond trees and silver-green groves of twisted old olives. There were well-pruned vineyards and rows of leafy fig trees laden with ripening fruit and the flame-flowered pomegranates. And in the hollows between the hills lay well-watered green pastures where flocks of fat sheep and bleating lambs grazed peacefully while their shepherds stood guard with their crooks or sat playing rustic and reedy music on their pipes. And one stood singing:

> *The Lord is my shepherd*
> *I shall not want*
> *He maketh me to lie down in green pastures . . .*

Everywhere flowers bloomed in the fields and by the peaceful farmhouses: roses and oleanders, white jasmine and yellow mimosa, and their fragrance rose up in the air with the smoke of the hearths and the song of the lark and the call of the cuckoo to the high blue sky where small clouds sailed, molten gold in the morning sunlight.

And Naomi said: "Is it now to be wondered that Balaam said when King Balak of Moab called him to curse the Israelites:

> *How goodly are thy tents, O Jacob,*
> *And thy tabernacles, O Israel!*"

And they came to a flourishing garden of vegetables with a fig tree whose fruit was ripe, and Naomi said: "I am hungry for fresh food, let us go in and eat."

And Ruth said: "Hast thou no fear that the owner of the garden may come? In Moab the owner would whip you for trespassing."

And Naomi said: "Moses said, *When thou comest into thy neighbor's vineyard, then thou mayest eat grapes thy fill at thine own pleasure; but thou shalt not put any in thy vessel.* And this he said on the way here, long before the Israelites had any vineyards."

So they turned into the garden and ate their fill of figs and vegetables and then they went on.

And when they passed a house where a woman sat milking the goats for her children who stood waiting around her, "Peace unto you!" she cried to them, offering them of the milk; and they answered, "To you, peace!" and they stopped and drank gratefully of the milk and the woman looked with curiosity upon the golden amulets Ruth wore until Ruth said to her that she was from Moab. Then the woman turned from Ruth and pointed to a pillar of smoke rising up from the valley northward toward Debir and she told with bitterness how the Moabite raiders had destroyed a defenceless village in the night. The inhabitants they had killed or driven away; and in their fields not a stem, not a blade of grass was left; for what the camels of the Moabites had not devoured their broad hoofs had trampled down. And Ruth was sorely distressed at the woman's tale.

Then one of the small boys, bright eyed and curly haired, held up for her to see the bow and arrow he was fashioning. "Have you seen any raiders?" he asked. "This is for the Philistine giants." And he let fly an arrow at a tree.

And Naomi said to Ruth as they went on: "Thus from childhood are the men of Israel divided in their spirits, dreaming and speaking of peace and preparing for war. For as Balaam rightly said, *It is a people that dwell alone.* They are encircled by enemies. Marauders come not only from Moab on the east but from Ammon too, and from the Philistines on the west and from the Arameans on the north and from Edom and Midian and Amalek on the south. And though the Israelites have been commanded by Moses to consider kindly the stranger among them it is understandable, is it not, my daughter, that they look with suspicion upon the stranger among them."

And Ruth said sadly: "It is indeed understandable. And I am prompted to remove the amulets from my brow which mark me for a stranger; but I am loath to do so out of fear."

And Naomi said: "Nor would I have you who came here out of love do anything out of fear in Israel. But consider that we have enemies in our very midst! See there where the Jebusites live on the border between Judah and Benjamin!" And she pointed up to where the bastioned walls of Jerusalem rose like a crenelated crown from the hills, gleaming in the golden sunlight.

And so they came toward noon to the road running by the great wall of Jerusalem high and mighty with its two tall gate towers, the Gate of Gihon and the Gate of the Fountain. And the highway was busy with travelers. Many went in and out of the gates of the city of the Jebusites; and there was a constant throng of those traveling to and from the Israelite towns along the highway—northward to Gibeah and Bethel in Benjamin and to Shiloh in the hill country of Ephraim and far beyond to the land of Dan with great wagons for the cedars of Lebanon; and southward to Bethlehem in Judah, and to Hebron and Beersheba on the way down into Egypt with merchant caravans. And it was easy to distinguish which were the Israelites among the travelers, because, as Naomi pointed out to Ruth, these wore fringes at the four corners of their garments in accordance with the instructions of Moses— which Elimelech and his sons had not adhered to in Moab because of their fear of being marked as strangers among the Moabites.

And as Ruth and Naomi approached the city they saw that on top of the thick wall of Jerusalem was gathered a crowd of the Jebusites; for there by the roadside, to divert passers-by and to gather some shekels from them, a troupe of traveling storytellers had made their stage against the great stones of the wall in a recess between two bastions of the Gate of the Fountain. They were strangely garbed as if in the raiment of other times and places; and they played out their stories in pantomime accompanied by the music of reeds and cymbals.

The two women stopped their donkeys on the edge of the throng of passers-by which had gathered to watch the play of the storytellers, some standing, some seated upon their camels and donkeys.

"These storytellers are Israelites," said Naomi to Ruth, to whom it was altogether strange; "and they are playing out parts of the story of the children of Israel. This one they are telling now is the end of the story of Jacob. See, it is just as I told you. Old Jacob, sitting upon his bed, crosses his arms to place his right hand on the head of the younger of the two sons of Joseph, who stands there behind them dressed like an Egyptian prince. See, he is trying to prevent his father from exchanging the blessings, although he himself was the youngest of Jacob's sons. But the old man insists on having it his way—on giving the first blessing to Ephraim the younger. And now Jacob draws his feet up on the bed and dies."

With a long wailing of the reeds, the story came to an end. And the Jebusites on top of the wall cheered loudly, while the Israelites in the throng below lamented the death of their patriarch. And one of these standing nearby and observing the two women turned to Naomi and said: "Are you a woman in Israel?" And she said: "That I am." And he said: "Then why do you go about with this strange woman?" And Naomi said: "She is no longer a strange woman; she has become one of us." And the man said: "Then why does she wear those amulets of Ashtar?"

And Ruth answered him saying: "It is because of my husband who used to wish me to wear these charms to please him though he was an Israelite living in Moab."

Then the man said contemptuously to Naomi: "That comes of our having to do with strangers; they corrupt us to their ways. We cannot change them to ours. It is no use your telling her our story."

And Naomi said to Ruth: "Come, my daughter, let us be on our way."

But Ruth said: "Nay, let us remain, for I have never seen the like of these storytellers in Moab. Let us make our noonday meal here and watch their next play."

So they waited and ate while the players removed Jacob's deathbed and set up wooden pillars and beams giving the semblance of a room in a house with two doorways, an outer and an inner one; and they brought a rude couch and close by it they set up a weaver's loom, its two posts sunk into the ground. And close by the loom they placed a huge pair of shears.

"But why do not the players speak?" asked Ruth. "It must be difficult for those who are not Israelites and have no knowledge of these tales to understand the unspoken story. Surely those Jebusites had no understanding of what had happened when they cheered the death of old Jacob."

"They understood very well," said Naomi, "and they cheered out of their hatefulness toward Israel. And though these stories are being played out under the walls of the city of the Jebusites it is not for them they are meant but for the Israelites who take this road traveling between the tribes and to and from their tabernacle in Shiloh where they go to sacrifice to the Lord God of Israel. And for them the stories need not be spoken; they are reminders of tales from our Book of Remembrance, tales that had been told them since childhood—reminders that they must not turn aside from their way into the gates and the ways of the Jebusites and the other peoples that revile the way of Israel."

And Ruth said: "I shall learn all the story of Israel, which is from henceforth my people. And now thou wilt tell me this one as it is played."

For the music had begun with a loud clash of cymbals and on to the stage strode five foreign princes, richly dressed and armed, each bearing a bag of clinking silver. And one knocked at the outer doorway and they entered the house. Then to the strains of seductive music a woman appeared at the inner door. And she was beautiful and evil, and an avid smile lighted her painted eyes as she listened to the princes who displayed the silver in their bags while they whispered to her.

And Ruth was curious about all this, but Naomi remained silent. "Tell me, Naomi," begged Ruth, "tell me who she is and what they are telling her."

And Naomi said, though she seemed loath now to speak, "She is Delilah the Philistine woman and they are the Philistine princes who are offering her, each one, eleven hundred shekels of silver if she will seduce Samson the strong man of Israel and discover for them the secret of his strength."

Ruth said: "Then this is the story of that unwise hero whom thou didst mention to me one day on the way but of whom thou didst say no more."

And the Israelite standing nearby them said: "He was indeed unwise to have had any traffic with the likes of her; and if I had my way no strange woman would be permitted to enter the land of Israel."

50

And Naomi said to him: "Then it is well that you do not have your way." And to Ruth she said: "Yes it is the story of Samson the Strong who once roamed these very hills. And now that we have eaten let us go on, and I shall tell you the tale some other time."

"But now," said Ruth, "I do understand the play. See, Delilah agrees to do what they wish. And she hides the Philistine princes in the inner chamber; for there comes Samson. Is he not wonderful!"

And he was indeed wonderful to behold. To loud victorious music came a monstrous man with bare brawny arms and massive thighs, clad in a tawny lion's skin that barely served to cover the half of his mighty chest and his manhood. His thick black hair hung down from his head in seven long plaits. At his waist he wore for a weapon the white jawbone of a beast. And on his muscular back he bore two great iron gates.

And Ruth asked: "Why is he clothed in that skin and armed with that bone, Naomi; and why does he carry those gates?"

And Naomi said: "The skin is that of the lion he tore in two with his bare hands when it roared at him in the vineyard of Timnah. And the bone is the jawbone of an ass with which he smote thousands of Philistines at Lehi; he rose up and laid them out in heaps upon heaps, after his own men had bound and delivered him to the Philistines who then ruled over Israel. And the gates on his back are the gates of Gaza wherein the Philistines thought they had trapped him one night while he lay there with a harlot—for Samson was a too lusty Israelite—but he arose at midnight and laid hold of the city gates and plucked them up, bars and all, and carried them off."

"And now," said Ruth, "she is enticing him in to tell

her the secret of his strength." For Delilah bared her breasts and took up a lyre and went to stand at the outer door of her house and, to the strains of her seductive music, she caught and held the eyes of that mighty Israelite, who, when he saw her beauty and the welcome in her eyes, cast off like toys the gates from his shoulders and followed her into the house and to her couch where Delilah soon lay in his lusty embrace. And she stroked the sinews of his arms, admiring his power and entreating him to tell her its secret until he whispered indulgently into her ear.

"What is he telling her, Naomi? Tell me what he is telling her," pleaded Ruth.

Then Naomi said: "Samson said to Delilah: *If they bind me with seven green withes that were never dried, then shall I become weak, and be as another man.*"

And Ruth said: "Was it so, Naomi? Was that truly the secret?"

Naomi said: "Wait and you shall see."

And Delilah pillowed the head of Samson on her soft breast and played him sweet music until he fell fast asleep. Then Delilah rose up and called the Philistine princes from the inner room and whispered to them what Samson had told her. And they hurried away and returned quickly with seven green withes and bound the sleeping man and went to hide again in the inner room while Delilah roused Samson to the sound of the cymbals striking a wild alarum. And Samson woke; and as he stretched his powerful limbs the green withes broke like strings of tow touched by fire. And he laughed uproarously at Delilah's test of his strength; but she was sorely displeased with his mocking, so he took her again into his great arms, and again she entreated him to tell her the secret of his strength until again he whispered to her.

Then Ruth said: "What is he telling her this time, Naomi?"

And Naomi answered her: "Wait and you shall see."

And again Delilah pillowed the head of Samson upon her bare breast until he fell into deep sleep, and she arose and called the Philistines from the inner chamber and whispered to them what Samson had told her; and they went out and returned with a length of new rope and they bound Samson fast with it as he slept. Then they returned to their hiding place and again Delilah woke Samson to the warning sound of the cymbals; and he stretched out his arms and broke the thick new rope like thread, laughing aloud at her amazement. But this time she was so displeased at his deceit of her that he could not cajole her into his arms again. She turned away angrily from him and went to the loom nearby and began weaving a web, passing the shuttle swiftly back and forth and beating the strands together with the pin. Then Samson stood up and went behind Delilah and put his strong arms about her to make love to her, but she heeded him not and continued her weaving until he whispered again into her ear.

"What is he telling her now, Naomi?" asked Ruth fearfully. "Surely he will not tell her the truth this time."

Naomi said: "Wait and see."

And Delilah, listening to Samson's whispering, smiled again and went with him to the couch and fondled him there until he fell into deep sleep again. Then she rose up and went to his head and unbraided, one by one, the seven thick plaits of his long black hair and spread it out to the loom and drew the hairs in with the warp and wove them into her web, beating the shuttling weft with the pin to hold them tightly. And in their hiding place the watching Philistines drew their swords as Delilah, to the loud crashing of the cymbals, roused Samson again. And he raised up his head and turned it, and the loom came away from its place, its posts plucked from the earth, with its beams, the pin and the woven web, all hanging from the head of Samson. And mighty Samson, laughing aloud, swung and rattled the loom about his head like a toy; but Delilah wept and would not be consoled until Samson contritely called her to him and whispered again to her, this time very earnestly.

And Ruth said anxiously to Naomi: "Now he is telling her the truth; is he not, Naomi?"

Naomi said: "Yes, he is telling her the truth. For the power of a woman lies not in might but in patience and persistence."

And now Delilah, after sporting with Samson a while, bid him rest his head on her knees and she sang him to sleep; and then she called the five Philistines to her and made them give her their bags of silver before she would tell them what Samson had said.

"She is sure he has told her the truth this time," said Ruth sadly.

Naomi said: "Yes, she knows she has won."

Then Delilah motioned to one of the Philistines to bring her the huge pair of shears. And she cut Samson's long black hair and it fell away from his head with the loom, and one of the Philistines shaved it all short with his sword. Then Delilah shook Samson while the cymbals clashed again, and Samson woke up with a start and seeing the Philistines close upon him he tried to rise up; but his strength had gone from him and he could not, though he shook his head hard and flailed his great arms.

And Naomi said bitterly: "The strong man's weakness is in his head."

And seeing him helpless, four of the Philistines fell

54

upon Samson and held him fast while one took his spear and put out both Samson's eyes. And Samson howled in agony. And then to the sound of sad music the blind and broken man was led away, and the Jebusites sitting on top of the city wall howled with great glee and jeered down at the Israelites.

And one of them spying Ruth in the crowd below shouted down to her: "You there with the golden amulets —what are you doing among the accursed Israelites? Come in to us, my pigeon. You are too pretty for them!"

Ruth gave no heed to the Jebusite, but the Israelite standing beside her said: "Go in to the Jebusites; you will be more at home with them than with us."

And Ruth said to him: "I have heard that Moses instructed the children of Israel, when they were yet wanderers in the desert, to deal justly with the stranger who comes to sojourn among them. Is it possible that thou hast not heard of his teaching?" And when the man, abashed, had moved away from beside her she returned to watching the players, who came and removed the couch and the broken loom and set up the pillars and beams otherwise, in the semblance of a single large room. And a crowd of the players came dancing among the pillars to merry music and others climbed up on the roof beams to sit there looking down on the merrymakers.

Naomi said: "It is the Philistines in the temple of Dagon at Gaza rejoicing that their god has delivered their powerful enemy Samson into their hands."

And Ruth said: "See, there are the five Philistine princes and deceitful Delilah is with them."

Presently Samson was led into the temple like a huge captive beast, chained hand and foot, naked but for a loin cloth; and a new growth of hair hung ragged about his

55

head and before his sightless eyes. And the Philistines stood him between two of the pillars, to which they fixed his chains, and they bid him dance to the music for their entertainment. And Samson did as he was bid, lumbering about like a blind dancing bear with his heavy chains. And the Philistines perched on the roof beams of the temple laughed loud at his antics, and so did the Jebusites perched on the wall of Jerusalem, until Samson, raising his blinded eyes in supplication to heaven, put out his huge hands and took hold of the two pillars and pressed upon them, the one with his right hand and the other with his left. And he bowed himself with all his might which had returned to him with his hair, and the pillars parted and toppled and the roof beams of the temple with all the people perched upon them fell down upon Samson and the crowd of Philistines, upon the princes and the people about him, Delilah among them, and killed them all. And mighty Samson lay among the many dead he had made, as the play came to an end with mournful music, which was almost drowned out by the Jebusites up on the city wall who shouted down in anger at the Israelites, jeering at them and cursing.

Then Ruth, her dark eyes filled with tears, turned to Naomi and said: "Why do the Israelites tell this unhappy tale of their unwise hero before hateful strangers?"

And Naomi answered her: "Because they fear the hatred of those strangers less than the seduction of their women, and this tale is told and retold wherever the men of Israel go, as warning to them of the wiles of a strange woman, as a reminder to make them look with distrust upon all strange women. Though nothing is said of the foolishness of a hero who will let himself be so deceived and betrayed not by one woman but by two." And she told Ruth how Samson had also been intrigued by the Philistine woman of Timnah into telling the answer to his riddle of the lion and the honey: *Out of the strong comes forth sweetness.*

And Naomi said: "I have been loath to tell you the tale of Samson because you, too, are a strange woman in Israel; but it is just as well that you know it now; for you, my daughter, will have to contend with that distrust. But perhaps, with my help," and then her old eyes twinkled shrewdly, "it can be overcome. Perhaps we shall give them a happier story of a strange woman; and perhaps in times to come they will tell and retell with delight the story of Ruth."

But Ruth's dark eyes looked doubtful. For, the play having ended, the throng on the road was dispersing and the Israelites as they passed Ruth cast curious glances upon her, glances in which she saw that distrust and that fear of the strange woman which the story had stirred up in them.

Then Naomi, observing that many of the Israelites were carrying lambs as if for sacrifice, stopped one of them and inquired what was the occasion. And the man looked at her in amazement saying scornfully: "Is it possible that you are a woman in Israel and do not know that this is the week of the Passover! And tonight is the feast. These are the paschal lambs! Perhaps you have been consorting too much with strangers to remember such things!" And casting a contemptuous look upon Ruth he rode away.

And Naomi said to Ruth: "In Moab we could not observe this festival which celebrates the flight from Egypt of Moses and the children of Israel. And I had indeed forgotten that it came in this month. But let us hasten now to Bethlehem and perhaps we shall arrive there in time for the Passover feast. We shall go to the house of Elimelech's rich kinsman Tobias—who made the finest feast in Bethlehem every year. We could well do with a feast, after all that we have come through."

So they turned southward and urged their donkeys, the dove-gray and the milk-white one, along the road to the city of Bethlehem.

At sunset that evening when lamps were lit in the houses of Bethlehem the celebration of the Passover began. And nowhere was the festival better observed than in the house of Tobias, the richest merchant in the city. His house was the largest in Bethlehem, built of burnt brick with a high roof of cedar from Lebanon and set in a walled garden. Upon its massive doorposts were carved the ten commandments of the Lord God of Israel, in accordance with the words of Moses who said: *And thou shalt write them upon the doorposts of thy house.* And within the house of Tobias was much fine furniture, delicately carved and gilded tables and chairs and couches, some bought by Tobias in Egypt and some made for Tobias by his own artisans; and there were rich rugs and dyed stuffs and wrought silver brought by his caravans from Damascus and by his ships from Tyre.

Tobias himself was a paunchy and somewhat pompous man with beady brown eyes and a graying beard. And though Tobias, when he went to trade in Egypt, used to square the corners of his beard in the manner of the Egyptians, despite the injunction of Moses, he was always mindful of the favor the Lord God of Israel had shown him. And he had seen to it that his house was prepared for the Passover even more scrupulously than the Lord had ordained it. Tobias was a widower; but there were many women in his household, his daughters and daughters-in-law and his maidservants; and he had made certain that they had cleansed the house of every vestige of leavened bread, and had properly laid the long table for the Passover feast, covered it with snow-white damask and set upon it two tall seven-branched candelabra of bronze, and platters of unleavened bread, and jars of wine and chased-silver wine cups and a great salver of silver bearing the roasted shank bone of the paschal lamb and roasted eggs and bitter herb roots and fresh green herbs and a thick sweet sauce of chopped fruits and nuts in a silver dish and a silver bowl of salted water.

And when the women had lit the lamps of the candelabra Tobias took his place, reclining on a cushioned couch at the head of the great gleaming table, and he called all the family and friends he had gathered for the feast to take their places, each with a soft silken pillow to lean upon.

There were Tobias' sons and daughters and his sons-in-law and his daughters-in-law and his grandchildren; and there were several of his near kinsmen and among these was Boaz, a wealthy farmer whom Tobias would have liked to see married to his youngest and only remaining unmarried daughter Reba. For Boaz was valiant as well as wealthy—a hero of more than one battle with Israel's enemies. And for his heroic leadership Boaz had been made a judge in Judah—and Tobias, whose far-flung business often brought him into litigation, could well do with a judge in his family.

And Boaz had brought with him two of his young men, Elias, his able foreman and Gibbor the mightiest of his workers, a Benjamite who had come to sojourn in Judah.

And these three sat at the foot of the table, Boaz and his two friends, Elias and Gibbor the Benjamite, who were quite unlike: for cool-eyed Elias who sat on the right hand of Boaz was a slender man, austere, abstemious, pallid and stern of mien, earnest, upright and self-restrained; while red-haired and hairy-handed Gibbor who sat to the left of Boaz was a powerful ruddy-faced fellow, a lusty lover of fleshly things. And manly Boaz between them was unlike either of them, yet he partook of something of each. He was tall and well made, robust and lusty, a hearty and handsome man in his prime, with thick black hair glinting red where it curled on his head and beard; yet his grave gray eyes and tender mouth revealed the earnest, upright and self-restrained spirit within. And when they were seated and waiting for Tobias to begin the Passover rite Boaz turned to cool-eyed Elias and said: "You are required to drink at least five cups of wine with this feast"; and to Gibbor who reached at once for his goblet with his hairy left hand—for like many of the Benjamites Gibbor was left-handed—Boaz said: "But not to get drunk."

Whereupon Gibbor chuckled and said: "That is not likely with the Gadfly around." And he waved his wine cup at a man who sat near the head of the table on the right hand of Tobias: a lean and hungry-looking fellow with unkempt hair, his coarse garment tied about his waist with a length of rope. Long frayed fringes dangled from the corners of his garment, and two small clay tablets were bound with thongs to his brow and his bare left arm each bearing the ten commandments of the Lord God of Israel, in strict accordance with the words of Moses, who had said: *And thou shalt bind them for a sign upon thine hand, and they shall be for frontlets between thine eyes.* The man was Zvuv, well named the Gadfly, a prophet of the neighborhood who, having no gainful occupation, was usually famished, and now sat looking with longing at the fragrant food the women had prepared and were carrying in from the kitchen. But Zvuv, his restless Adam's apple bobbing up and down in his long bony neck, had to wait.

For one of the grandchildren, a bright-eyed boy named Joel, raised up his childish voice and, pointing to the things on the table, began asking questions of Tobias: "Why is this night so different from all other nights of the year? On all other nights we eat either leavened or unleavened bread: why then on this night do we eat only unleavened bread? On all other nights we eat herbs of any kind we like: why then on this night must we eat the bitter herbs? On all other nights we never dip herbs in water or in anything else: why then on this night shall we dip sweet green herbs in salted water and bitter herbs in sweet sauce, as Mother has instructed me. And on all other nights everyone sits up straight at the table: why then on this night do we all recline at our ease?" The boy ceased speaking with a sigh of relief, for he had spent his breath.

Then, while hungry Zvuv sat sniffing the waiting food in torment, Tobias asked Boaz to answer the childish questions: "For is not our kinsman Boaz a learned judge in Israel?" said Tobias ingratiatingly.

Then Boaz stood up in his place and spoke to young Joel and the other children saying: "It is said in our Book of Remembrance: *And it came to pass on the day when the Lord spake unto Moses in the land of Egypt, that the Lord spake unto Moses, saying, I am the Lord: speak thou unto Pharaoh king of Egypt all that I speak unto thee. And Moses said before the Lord, Behold, I am of un-*

62

circumcised lips, and how shall Pharaoh hearken unto me?"

And the children listened to Boaz but hungry Zvuv halted him saying: "Do we not all know what is in the Book of Remembrance, and as for the children let them be taught by their parents as Moses commanded."

But Boaz rebuked him saying: "Did not Moses say: *And thou shalt tell thy son in that day, saying, it is because of that which the Lord did for me when I came forth out of Egypt.* Now therefore let us show these children what happened. I shall be Moses and you shall be Pharaoh and Gibbor here shall be Aaron my brother." And as Zvuv sat fuming with angry impatience and the children watched wide eyed, Boaz pleaded with hard-hearted Pharaoh to let his enslaved people go and he turned to Aaron saying: *Take thy rod and cast it down before Pharaoh, that it become a serpent.* And Gibbor the Benjamite did so, using his brawny arm for the rod and making his muscles writhe to the delight of the children. Then Boaz told how when Pharaoh's magicians did likewise with their rods, Aaron's rod swallowed up all their rods. And how, Pharaoh's heart still being stubborn, Moses brought on the ten plagues: first, turning the river Nile to blood so that the fish died therein and the river stank; second, bringing a plague of frogs which swarmed into the houses and upon the beds and in the ovens and the kneading troughs of the Egyptians; and third, changing the dust of the earth to lice which covered both man and beast; and fourth, bringing the swarm of flies that corrupted the whole land of Egypt; and fifth, the murrain upon the cattle in the field and upon the horses, the asses and the camels, killing the herds and the flocks of Egypt while those of the Israelites lived; and sixth, sprinkling

63

ashes in the air that spread all over the land bringing boils breaking forth upon man and beast so that even Pharaoh's magicians could not stand before Moses because of their sores; and seventh, the storm of hail smiting all that was in the field, both man and beast, and every herb of the field and every tree, except in the land of Goshen where the children of Israel were; and eighth, the locusts eating every herb of the land and all the fruit of the trees which the hail had left until there remained not any green thing through all the land of Egypt; and ninth, the darkness over the land, for three days, a thick darkness which could be felt so that the Egyptians saw not one another for three days while all the children of Israel had light in their dwellings.

And Boaz showed how Moses stood before Pharaoh each time Pharaoh called him, promising to let the children of Israel go; and, pointing at sullen Zvuv, Boaz told how each time Pharaoh hardened his heart again when the plague had been lifted; until the tenth and last, when the Lord came at midnight and destroyed the first-born in the house of every Egyptian from Pharaoh the king to the lowliest among them, and the Angel of Death passed over the houses of the children of Israel which they had marked with the blood of the paschal lambs as Moses instructed them.

"And then," said Boaz to the children, "only then did fearful Pharaoh let the children of Israel go free. And that is why this night which we call the Passover is different from all other nights. And it is said in our Book of Remembrance that the people took their dough before it was leavened, their kneading troughs being bound up in their clothes upon their shoulders. And the children of Israel, fleeing in haste from the wrath of Egypt's cruel king Pharaoh, had no time to leaven and bake in their ovens the dough they had prepared for the journey but had to let it bake in the hot desert sun as they carried it on their backs, making just such flat unleavened cakes as we eat here tonight."

Then Tobias distributed pieces of the unleavened bread to all around the long table. And Zvuv ate ravenously, eyeing the fragrant food the women brought in while Boaz continued to answer the questions of Joel.

And why did they eat especially the bitter herbs on this night? To remind them of the bitterness of the lives of the children of Israel as slaves in Egypt, building vast pyramids and palaces, said Boaz; and Tobias passed to each one at the table a bit of the bitter herb.

And why did they dip the herbs twice that night? The bitter herb they dipped in the sweet sauce, thick as mortar, to recall how the bitterness of the lives of their forefathers as slaves in Egypt was overcome by the sweetness of the hope of freedom even as they had mixed the mortar for their cruel masters; and the sweet green herbs they dipped in salt water, Boaz told the children as Tobias passed them the aromatic sprigs, because this festival of freedom came in the springtime when all green growing life is renewed by the life-giving waters of winter seasoned with the salt of the earth. So all at the table dipped and ate the two herbs, first the bitter and then the green, the one in the thick sweet sauce and the other in salt water.

And finally, said Boaz, his grave gray eyes bright as those of the children who hung on his words, why did they all recline at table this night? As a sign of the freedom and well-being vouchsafed to the children of Israel by their One God, the God of their fathers, of Abraham and Isaac and Jacob, who had come from this land and whose children had returned to it out of bondage.

Then Tobias said a prayer of thanksgiving to the Lord God of Israel, the Almighty One who created the fruit of the vine, while the silver cups were filled to their brims with wine and everyone drank.

And the women brought ewers of water and basins for the washing of hands. And Tobias motioned to his daughter Reba to wait upon Boaz, who received her services with pleasure, for Boaz had an eye for beauty and Reba was a pretty sight in the rich raiment her father had given her for this feast. Then the women brought the good food to the table and served it for all to eat.

And all at the table were joyous—all but Zvuv, the prophet, who, even as he wolfed the rich food set before him, complained bitterly that they, the children of Judah, had not gone this year up to the tabernacle at Shiloh to celebrate the Passover before the Lord God of Israel as Moses had instructed all the children of Israel to do saying: *Three times in a year shall all thy males appear before the Lord thy God in the place which he shall choose: in the feast of unleavened bread, and in the feast of weeks, and in the feast of tabernacles.*

And when Tobias answered him that they dared not leave Bethlehem this Passover for fear of the marauding Moabites who had destroyed the village to the north near Debir, Zvuv said: "It is because of the backsliding of the children of Israel that the marauders have come, as it has always been in the past." And he murmured, between mouthfuls, of the wrongdoing of the children of Israel in these latter days, sparing not even his host as he spoke of the avarice of the rich, of their lack of true charity which the Lord God of Israel had said was no more than justice to the poor.

Nevertheless Tobias good-naturedly handed him stuffed

fish which had been caught that very day in the Great Sea at Joppa and brought alive in salt water on his swift camels to Bethlehem.

"Do not think," said Zvuv, gobbling the savory fish, "that I am deceived," dropping his angry phrases between delicious bites, "by your generosity to me. As it is said:

> *The rich man is wise in his own eyes;*
> *But the poor man that hath understanding searcheth*
> *him through.*

You have me here at your table, Tobias, for the sake of your conscience. But that will not save you. And all the generosity of the rich will not atone for their avarice, without which they could not be rich and would not be generous."

And Tobias, trying to keep Zvuv's mouth filled, helped him to more of the fish and said indulgently, "Nevertheless as the old saying puts it: *The poor man is not popular among his neighbors but the rich man hath many friends.* And are you not being too hard on the rich? For is not the proverb true: *The rich and the poor together, the Lord is the maker of us all?*"

And Zvuv still eating industriously answered him: "Put not your trust in proverbs, while with your wealth you try to influence and corrupt the judges in the city gates." And Zvuv turned then to Boaz at the foot of the table, complaining loudly of the lack of judgment and honesty of two of the three judges who held court at the city gates, warning Boaz—whom grudgingly he excepted from his charge—that Tobias was trying to get into his good graces because of a trial he had coming up soon with his workmen. And Boaz laughingly assured Zvuv that nothing could influence his judgment; that his judgment could no more be swayed by the hospitality of his kinsman Tobias than were the opinions of Zvuv himself.

But Zvuv undeterred returned to berating Tobias. "And see how with your wealth you enhance the vanity of your women who think only of fine raiment and adornment. Look at them!" And he ceased eating the roast lamb, which had been handed him, only long enough to wave his fork contemptuously at the women, all plump and sparkling with jewels, who gave not the slightest heed to him as they talked noisily amongst themselves while they happily fed their men, their children, and themselves the plentiful food they had made. Alas, no one in Bethlehem gave any more heed to the complaints of Zvuv than to the buzz of a gadfly. Nevertheless he persisted between strangling swallows of meat, saying: "Nor do the rich women care for their less fortunate sisters, the poor who must go gleaning in the fields and there become the wanton prey of the sinful men of the soil," and Zvuv raised up his voice so that his words could be heard by the three farmers at the foot of the table, by handsome Boaz and cool-eyed Elias who as they ate heartily talked of the barley harvesting to begin on the morrow, and by hairy-handed Gibbor who raised his eyes from his meat only to drink more wine and look lustfully upon the younger of the women, especially upon Reba, the youngest of the daughters of Tobias. And neither did these three men heed the talk of Zvuv; and Gibbor, to drown him out, set the wine-cheered sons and sons-in-law of Tobias to singing to their women:

As a lily among the thorns,
So is my love among the daughters.

To which the women responded:

As the apple tree among the trees of the wood,
So is my beloved among the sons.
I sat down under his shadow with great delight,
And his fruit was sweet to my taste. . . .

But the angry man of God lifted his voice yet louder to speak of the whoredom of the men of Israel, saying: "You go up into Jerusalem that is Jebus and there join the Jebusites in their abominations and then bring their ways into the cities and the fields of Israel." And when he began telling how the farmers of Dan, in the north, hoping to increase their crops thereby, had set up a high place to Baal and Ashtar and held an abominable orgy in a grove, Tobias hastily instructed his daughter Reba to take the eagerly listening children from the table and feed them in another room.

Yet Zvuv, undeterred, and still gobbling his meat with gusto pressed on, turning his tirade now upon Boaz alone, blaming him for his failure to restrain the men in his fields, saying: "I have myself seen them shamelessly lying there with the women. More than once have I seen there this son of Benjamin going after the women," and he pointed to Gibbor who was still lustily singing.

Then did Boaz turn from talking to Elias and he listened to Zvuv. And when Zvuv ceased his speaking long enough to stuff more meat into his mouth, Boaz raised up his voice and spoke, but not in anger; and all at the table, the men and the women, stopped their singing and gave heed to manly Boaz, who said: "I am a lover of freedom, Zvuv. And are we not all of us, children of Israel, lovers of liberty? And did not Moses, our great prophet and leader say: *Proclaim liberty throughout the land, to all the inhabitants thereof.* And do we not on this very night— as I have told the small children—do we not celebrate our freedom? And is it not true that since our fathers took flight with Moses from their bondage to mighty Pharoah in Egypt we have had no one man to command us? There is no king in Israel and every man does what is right in his own eyes. We have only judges to remind men of the laws of the Lord God of Israel which Moses brought down to us. And for my part I see to it that there is no Baal worship on my land and that no woman is forced in my fields to do other than she wishes. Even Moses who knew well that men can be enslaved and destroyed by their desires gave us no law that a man and a woman may not lie together in a field if they so desire and do not thereby commit adultery. We are free men in Israel."

"And the women, too, are free," said Gibbor merry with wine and looking boldly at Reba, who had returned from feeding the children.

And Zvuv said angrily: "The Lord God of Israel is our king and he has given us his commandments, and the Lord our King does not look with indulgence upon the back-sliding spirit of man."

"But," said Boaz reasonably, "it is not yet entirely clear to us what is the will of the Lord God of Israel. For in our Book of Remembrance we are told that long ago when *the whole Earth was of one language and of one speech* and the people came together to build a tower to reach up to heaven then the Lord said, *Now nothing will be withholden from them,* and he confounded their language and scattered them abroad upon the face of the earth, as if jealously guarding his secrets from man who had reached up to him. Yet at his bidding did Moses go up onto Mount Sinai and spoke to him and brought down to us the knowledge of the Lord and bid us seek to know him and all his laws and to observe them. And again though we are told

70

that Zipporah the first wife of Moses was a woman of Midian, and that when he was leading our fathers into this land the Lord warned him saying, *Lest thou take of their daughters unto thy sons and their daughters go awhoring after their gods and make thy sons go awhoring after their gods,* yet did Moses himself thereafter take a Cushite woman for his wife and the Lord did not heed the complaint of Aaron the brother of Moses and Miriam his sister regarding that marriage, but he still favored Moses. And now too often do I find it difficult to know and to do what is right and to feel justified in judging another and telling him what to do and what not. I have heard it said by the wise that *the spirit of man is the lamp of the Lord searching all the inward parts,* and it seems to me that it is for each man to heed the commandments of the Lord as best he can, which is according to his own lights—according to the lamp of his spirit."

Zvuv, who had stopped eating to listen, his Adam's apple rising and falling impatiently, cried angrily: "Then tell me why have you not heeded the commandment: *Be fruitful and multiply!*—why is a man like you, young and strong and owning his fine fertile fields, why is he not yet married and the father of children in Israel—neither he nor his two young men?"

And Reba, standing nearby to Boaz, eagerly awaited his answer. And Tobias, too, stopped stroking his well-filled paunch and leaned forward to listen.

Then Boaz laughed gently before he answered, saying: "Though the Lord God of Israel has indeed counseled us to be fruitful, yet has he left a man free to choose when and with whom he shall marry and beget children for his inheritance. Jacob, the father of all Israel, did not marry until he found Rachel the woman he truly loved and he

71

worked seven years and then yet another seven to get her. As for Gibbor and Elias——"

And here Gibbor, who was drunk with wine, rose up and shouted: "You know very well that there are not enough women in Benjamin and that the other tribes of Israel have sworn not to give their daughters to us. Would Tobias give me his daughter, Reba? Would you Tobias?" And Tobias shook his head. "No. Then can you blame me if I take what I can get in the fields?"

And, in the silence that followed, cool-eyed Elias, who had drunk very little wine and was not given to gazing upon women, leaned over to Boaz and said: "Ask Zvuv now why he is not with his wife this Passover night. Can it be that he has heard the proverb: *It is better to dwell in the desert than with a fretful and contentious woman?* And ask him who provides for the children he has made and now neglects while he is so busy correcting the errors of others."

Zvuv answered with angry pride: "It is the business of the prophet who serves the Lord God of Israel to put the correction of his people before every other duty. Moses left his wife, Zipporah, and his two sons, Gershon and Eliezer, with Jethro his father-in-law in Midian while he went to lead the children of Israel up out of Egypt. And in times to come, the children of Israel will be known as the people of the prophets. Did not Moses say: *Would God that all the Lord's people were prophets?*"

"God forbid!" exclaimed Gibbor. "And in times to come the children of Israel will be descended from us, backsliders though we be, who enjoy the making of many children, and not from you, prophets, who are too busy running about on your loveless errand." And the men and women about the table laughed with Gibbor who sat down and reached for the wine again with his hairy left hand.

And Zvuv, sputtering with fury, was hastily swallowing the food in his mouth to make way for more angry words with which to answer him when Tobias hastily said: "It is time now to open the house door, as is our custom on this night, in memory of that time when we were wanderers and as a sign of welcome to any passing stranger, hungry or in want of shelter," and he poured a full goblet of wine to stand on the table as a symbol of that welcome. "Open the door now," he said to Reba; and his daughter went to open the house door, a little fearful of this rite—of what might be lurking outside. But there was nothing to be seen but the darkness of the night; and she stood drawing her robe about her to guard against the chill night air while she waited for her father to finish the salutation: ". . . whoever is hungry let him come in and eat!" which he hastily mumbled without looking at the door, for no one was ever expected.

And as Tobias ended, Zvuv drily remarked: "What poor man would venture to come unasked to the house of Tobias?"

But Reba, peering out into the starlit darkness cried: "Someone is coming! Look! There are two! Two women! They are tying their donkeys by the garden gate—one gray and one white!"

And in a moment Naomi appeared in the doorway, saying: "Peace unto you!" and behind her came Ruth.

Tobias looked up from the table at the old woman in her worn and bedraggled garments and he said: "Unto you peace!" and he asked: "Who are you?"

And the women of the household who went and peered at her as she entered the lighted room exclaimed:

"But it looks like our Naomi!"

"Is this Naomi?"

"Can this be Naomi who went to Moab with Elimelech and her sons?"

"But it cannot be!"

Yet, seeing that it was she, they embraced her. And Joel and the other children hearing their cries of welcome came running from the other room to see who had arrived.

And Naomi sadly nodded her head and she said: "But call me not Naomi, the sweet one, for my spirit is no longer sweet as when you knew me. Call me Marah, which means bitterness, for the Almighty has dealt very bitterly with me. I went out full, and the Lord has brought me home empty."

"And where is my kinsman, Elimelech?" asked Tobias, as the women hastened to make a place for her at the table.

"He died in Moab," said Naomi. "And our two sons also."

Then all turned to the dark doorway where stood Ruth, whose radiant beauty of face and form neither the shadows nor the sad state of her raiment could obscure. Beneath the gleaming golden amulets on her brow such as no woman in Israel wore, her dark eyes looked toward them, awaiting their welcome. And all their eyes were filled with curiosity. And Reba observed that the eyes of Boaz and his men were fixed upon her, Boaz sitting still in his place, but Gibbor standing up boldly, the better to see the strange woman.

"This is Ruth, my daughter-in-law," said Naomi.

"A woman of Moab!" exclaimed Zvuv, and he spat aside, as at something loathsome.

"But she is no longer of Moab," said Naomi firmly. "She is one of us."

"What do you mean? How can she be one of us!" said Zvuv contemptuously.

74

And Naomi said: "When I tried to persuade her from coming with me into Judah she said: Entreat me not to leave thee and to return from following after thee: For whither thou goest, I will go; and where thou lodgest, I will lodge. Thy people shall be my people, and thy God my God."

But Zvuv looked dubiously at Ruth, who still stood by the door, and Naomi said: "Come, Ruth, sit here beside me," and to the women she said: "We are weary and famished."

Then Ruth went to sit beside Naomi and the women brought food and placed it before them. And Reba brought the ewer of water for Naomi to wash her hands; but Reba did not offer the water to Ruth, as if Ruth, not being an Israelite, would not want it. And Naomi seeing Reba turn away said: "Bring Ruth the water. She will not eat without washing her hands as we do." But Reba made as if she had not heard and would have carried off the water had not Boaz got up from his place and taken the ewer from Reba and brought it to Ruth who, without lifting her dark eyes to him, said: "I thank thee," and washed her hands with the water.

Then Boaz returned to his place at the end of the table and sat staring at Ruth, his eyes filled with the faintly fearful fascination which her strange beauty stirred up in his heart—that strange beauty which was at once a promise of unknown delights and of unknown dangers.

Tobias was greatly displeased with Reba for what had happened; and he observed how the eyes of his unmarried nephew Namaan and even of the married men at the table had been drawn to the stranger. Displeasure and jealousy troubled the breast of Tobias as he considered the strange woman who had come into his house.

And Ruth could not eat for embarrassment, because of the looks of suspicion which the women cast upon her as they served her and because of the look of scorn in the burning eyes of Zvuv on the other side of the table.

But Naomi, eating heartily, told of their journey from Moab and how Ruth had routed the wild beasts with a sling and had saved her alive at the ford of Jordan. And even young Joel was entranced at the sight of Ruth and he stood staring at her, exclaiming to the other children: "Think of that—a woman who routed the wild beasts!"

And burly Gibbor the Benjamite, bent upon winning the favor of this strange and beautiful woman, came from his place beside Boaz to sit beside Ruth and brought to her in his big hairy hands the good things on the table beyond her reach. And he spoke softly to her, with ardent glances: "I have heard much of the Moabite maidens; but never before have I been near to one and known how beautiful they might be, and I'll be a son of Belial if I have ever seen a more beautiful maiden anywhere, even in Shiloh in the hill country of Ephraim where the maidens of Israel are most beautiful."

"Thou art kind to say so; but I am no longer a Moabitess," Ruth answered him, "nor am I any longer a maiden."

And Joel whispered to the other children: "See how strangely they speak in Moab, saying thou instead of you, much as Moses and the children of Israel used to speak in the old days!"

But the ardor of Gibbor the Benjamite was not easily rebuffed; and he took pleasure in the forthrightness of Ruth's rejoinder. "So much the better for me," Gibbor said, and he laughed aloud.

From the far end of the table the grave gray eyes of Boaz watched them with awakening jealousy. And the cool eyes of Elias were troubled by the disturbance he saw in the manly face of his friend.

And the eyes of Zvuv, seeing what was astir in the hearts of the men because of the advent of this strange woman among them, burned still more scornfully as he turned to Tobias and said: "The sons of Israel forget how mighty Samson was ensnared and betrayed to our enemies by a strange woman. Samson was also called ha-Gibbor, the Strong."

Then Gibbor stood up from beside Ruth.

And Naomi cried: "Hold your tongue, Zvuv! Did not the Lord say to Moses: *When a stranger shall sojourn with thee and will keep the Passover to the Lord, he shall be as one that is born in the land.*"

Zvuv said: "Moses meant that the stranger shall be circumcised first as we are. Moses said: *When a stranger shall sojourn with thee and will keep the Passover for thy Lord, let all his males be circumcised, and then let him come near and keep it.*"

And Naomi said: "Then I thank God that Ruth is a woman and cannot be circumcised in the flesh; but she is circumcised in her heart and spirit, and Moses, who married Zipporah the daughter of a Midianite priest, would surely have counted her one of us."

Zvuv said disdainfully: "My wife also thinks that she knows all the laws of Moses."

Whereupon Gibbor leaned across the table, threatening Zvuv with his great red-haired fist, and said: "Never mind about Moses! You hold that bitter tongue in your head, or I'll show you how strong I am! I'll be a son of Belial if I don't!"

Zvuv shouted: "You are a son of Benjamin, of whom his father Jacob said when he blessed his sons:

Benjamin is a wolf that raveneth;
In the morning he shall devour the prey,
And at even he shall divide the spoil."

And Gibbor would have struck Zvuv had not Boaz come from his place and restrained him. Whereupon cool-eyed Elias stood up and said: "Come, Boaz, we must gather the omer tonight—the first fruits of the barley harvest for the sacrifice."

And Boaz, looking angrily at Zvuv, left the table with Elias, and they both took hold of Gibbor by the arms and led him away with them.

Then Naomi asked Tobias: "Is that our kinsman, Boaz, who was a thin young stripling when I left Judah?"

"That is he," said Tobias.

"He has grown to a valiant fellow," said Naomi, looking after tall Boaz as the three men went out of the house.

"He has indeed," said Tobias. "He has been a strong defender of Judah against our enemies the Philistines who have troubled us often in the years since Samson brought the temple of Dagon down on the heads of their princes. And Boaz will lead us against the Moabites should they come again to molest us." And he paused with a glance at Ruth, but she sat silent with downcast eyes. "Now Boaz is a judge in Judah; the wisest of the three judges, and the most popular with the people. And he is the owner of broad rich fields; of many cattle and even horses, which are still very few in Israel. Boaz is a much-sought-after young man by the women of Bethlehem." Tobias spoke with the envy of an aging man. "He is much sought after, too, by the fathers of marriageable daughters. I should not mind having him for a son-in-law myself." And he looked reprovingly at Reba, his daughter.

Naomi said: "He reminds me of my Elimelech as he was when I married him. And did you not think him handsome?" she asked Ruth.

"I did not look upon him," Ruth said, and indeed her eyes were too full of tears to have seen Boaz had she looked. And she said: "I dearly wish to remain in Judah with you, Naomi; but I cannot stay here in a house where I am scorned. Is there no other place for us?"

Naomi said: "My home, the old house of Elimelech, so long neglected, is doubtless no more than a ruin." And she turned to Tobias: "Now tell me truly, Tobias, how you do feel in your heart about having us here in your household."

Then Tobias glanced at the scowling face of Zvuv, who was busily gathering leftovers from the table into his ragged kerchief, and Tobias said: "You, dear Naomi, the wife of my kinsman Elimelech, are surely most welcome. And what you tell of the loyalty and the fortitude of your daughter-in-law is indeed remarkable, though I must say, for my own part, that I look for other virtues in a woman. All the same, and no matter what you say of her, she is a Moabitess and I cannot prevent what will be thought and said of her here in Judah. Only yesterday came word of the band of marauders from Moab who burnt down a defenceless village to the north near Debir. And it is to be expected that there will be even more than the usual suspicion of anyone from Moab, not only in the town but in my own household."

And it was indeed plain enough in the faces of Reba and the rest of his womenfolk how they looked upon that strange beauty which had already stirred the men of Judah to strife in Ruth's behalf.

"Now mind you, I am not intolerant," Tobias continued, "for did not Moses command us to consider the

79

stranger among us; but he did so without considering the position we would be in, here in the land. Now there are bound to be troublesome difficulties and I do like peace in my household." Then Tobias turned to Ruth, saying as he stroked his paunch gently: "To be sure, if you wish to stay here——"

Ruth said softly: "I cannot stay here."

And Naomi rose up and said: "Indeed not! Nor can I! I would rather remain with you, Ruth, in a hovel, than in the rich house of a mealymouthed hypocrite who has engraved the law of the Lord on his gates but not in his heart. Surely we shall survive without his help. Come, my daughter, let us go now and see what remains of the house of Elimelech!"

They rode their donkeys, the dove-gray and the milk-white one, through the dark narrow streets of Bethlehem, quiet and empty in the festival night, past the windows of houses all cheerfully lighted for the Passover. And they crossed the market place, lying deserted now between the two city gates with their tall, massive towers, one round and one square, where sentinels stood watch on the heaps of round stones piled up for missiles in case of attack and for the execution of judgment upon evildoers condemned to stoning.

And they rode out through the right hand gate, the square stone Gate of the Judges before which stood the bench of the judges; and, after following a stony path that ran close outside the city wall, the two women came to the lightless ruin of a house on a hill. The late-rising moon sent beams through its broken walls; the stars shone down through holes in its sagging roof. A jackal howled, leaped out through a window and trotted away as they approached. When Naomi unlocked and opened the door a flock of bats flew out. And the rotted door which had come away from its hinges could not be closed again.

Then Ruth had to plead with frightened Naomi to enter after her. And in the moonlit darkness it was Ruth who made the bed on which the two weary women lay down. And she stayed awake, though her heart and her eyelids were heavy with sadness, talking bravely of what they would do on the morrow, until the old woman ceased her trembling. Then as they lay there in the darkness they heard the distant voices of men calling to each other, and Ruth asked, "What is that?"

And Naomi said: "They are gathering the omer, the first fruits of the harvest, which are set aside for an offering to the Lord God of Israel. For the men of Israel though they no longer sacrifice their first-born sons yet give up to their God the first fruits of their fields."

Then Ruth rose up from her bed and went to the broken door and looked out; and she saw in the valley below the men moving about in the moonlit fields, swinging sickles and scythes; and some were calling, and others answered the callers' questions, their strong voices rising up in the night to the moonlit heavens:

"Is the sun set?"

"Yea!"

"Is this a sickle?"

"Yea!"

"Is this a basket?"

"Yea!"

"Shall we reap!"

"Reap!"

"Let us reap for the Lord!"
And once again from a further field:
"Is the sun set?"
"Yea!"

Over and over they called and answered as they gathered
And there was a comfort in the manly strength of their
peaceful voices. And Ruth lay down again beside Naomi
who had fallen asleep; and she lay listening a long time to
those strange reapers. She lay looking out through the
open door at the strange moonlit land, its hills so different
from the wide wild plains of Moab, her dark eyes filled
with wonder before her destiny . . . until she, too, slept.

The two women rose up at dawn. The day was bright
and they set to work with a will, cleansing the long-neglected house and making such repairs as they could. They
took two water jars and brought water up from the well
at the foot of the hill. They washed the dust-covered
pottery and utensils in the kitchen; they heated the oven
for baking, ground grain in Naomi's stone quern, and
baked their own unleavened bread.

Naomi found her old loom and instructed Ruth in its
use; and Ruth said she would weave woolen curtains for
the door and the windows through which the chill night
wind had blown in upon them unhindered. And as they
worked Naomi sang for Ruth that old Israelite song she
had promised to teach her:

> *A woman of valor who can find?*
> *Her worth is far above rubies.*
> *The heart of her husband trusteth in her,*
> *And he shall lack for nothing.*
> *She doeth him good and not evil*
> *All the days of her life.*
> *She seeketh out wool and flax*

And worketh well with her hands.
She is like the fine ships
Bringing food from afar. . . .

And hearing their singing, the neighboring women on their way down to the well stopped to greet Naomi, and they spread the news of her coming at the well so that many others came up to welcome Naomi back to Bethlehem, and they brought her gifts of food; but all stared with suspicion upon the strange woman—the Moabitess whom Naomi had brought in among them, to become one of them.

And on that first day and in the days that followed, when Ruth took a tall jar and, carrying it gracefully upon her head in the manner of the women of Moab, went down to the well for water, she was looked upon curiously by the women gathered and gossiping there and by the children playing there with the fountain of water; but none spoke to her. And when she spoke to them none answered her, and some even mocked amongst themselves at her strange way of speaking.

One day Reba the daughter of Tobias was there, and she began speaking of Ruth to the others, saying: "Can it be that there are no men remaining in Moab, that their women must come with their golden charms to capture the men of Israel? . . ." until Ruth silenced her with a glance from her dark eyes that boded no good for Reba if she continued. Then Ruth spoke forthrightly: "Rest assured that I have no designs on the men of Israel, having left the husband I loved in a grave in Moab. It is for his memory alone, because they once pleased him, that I wear these charms. Surely you who live here under the wing of the Almighty God of Israel need have no fear of Ashtar, a goddess of Moab. And I came into the land of Israel because Mahlon weaned me away from the ways of Moab and taught me to love the ways of Israel, which he had kept in his heart. And you who are Israelites merely because you were born so have no cause to scorn one who has chosen to be an Israelite." Then she took up her water jar and left the chastened women at the well.

But it was more difficult to deal with the children playing about the well, who had been told by young Joel of the evil things he heard spoken about the Moabitess in the house of his grandfather, Tobias.

Led by Joel the children would follow after Ruth up the hill, whispering and pointing and mimicking her speech, until once she stopped and called them to her saying softly: "Come and speak to me, children, for I, too, am now one of the children of Israel, and I dearly wish I had children of my own like you, especially a lad like thee, Joel, whom I would teach to become a good Israelite, to learn the words of Moses and to obey the laws of the Lord God of Israel which tell thee to be good to the stranger among you."

"And would you teach him," asked Joel, "to sling stone as you did at the wild beasts on the way from Moab?"

"Indeed I would," answered Ruth, "and I will teach thee, too, if thou wishest." And Joel watched with delight as she took some tufts of wool left by passing sheep on the nearby thorn bushes and twisted them into cords and braided the cords into a stout strand flat and wide in the middle from which she made him a sling. And she showed him how to loop the ends over a finger and how she could hit a tree with a smooth round stone, which Joel promptly did also, to his own great wonder and satisfaction and the awe of the other children.

"Now let the Philistine giants come!" Joel cried, letting another stone fly at the tree with a resounding crash. And picking up still another stone he said: "And this is how I shall fight any raiding Jebusites or Ammonites or Moabites——" Whereupon he stopped and looked in confusion at Ruth.

And she said: "To be sure, whoever they are, if they come not with peace in their hearts but to molest thee, then sling it with all thy might!"

But, alas, on this try Joel's stone went wild and flew down to the well where it smashed the great jar of water which his aunt Reba had filled, and it deluged her dress. And then there was a great outcry from Reba and all the women with her at the well, calling the children away from the woman of Moab.

Yet thereafter, the innocent eyes of the children, having looked into the dark eyes of Ruth and seen there the truth and the goodness of her love for them and her longing for their love, they trooped after her up the hill, no longer whispering and pointing, but holding to her skirts and laughing and talking to her as if she were their mother. And she made them strange little Moabite cakes, crescents of crushed barley; and for the girls she shaped and baked and painted cunning clay dolls, and rattles of clay for the little ones. But their mothers, the neighboring women, took from the children the cakes and the toys for fear of some Moabite magic in the figures she made, thinking they might be figures of evil Ashtar.

And the heart of Naomi was saddened when she saw this; she was sorely troubled for the plight of Ruth in the face of that ancient fear and hatred of all Moab in the heart of Israel. And she was angered at the women, her neighbors, who chided her for bringing a Moabitess in to live among them; and because of her anger the women left off coming to Naomi and bringing her gifts of food. Then Naomi

85

became sorely troubled about her own plight; and one day, when Ruth gave to the hungry children, who despite their mothers still came running after her, some cakes she had made out of their scanty store of grain Naomi admonished Ruth, saying: "Where are we now to get our own livelihood?"

But Ruth was undismayed. And she said: "Is not the sun shining bright on the land of Israel, and is not the Lord God of Israel a good and bountiful God? Perhaps if we prayed to him or made some sacrifice—"

They were sitting on the step before the broken door in the pleasant spring sunshine, grinding the last of their corn, Naomi feeding the grains into the quern while Ruth worked the heavy grindstone with her young arms.

"Have I not taught you," said Naomi impatiently, "that the Lord God of Israel, unlike the gods other men have made, is not to be moved by wishful prayers or even sacrifices, which he accepts as his due; he is good and bountiful to those who know his laws and keep them faithfully. But unfortunately it is sometimes very difficult to know what his laws are. Especially for a woman," she added bitterly. "And when a woman is married it would seem that she suffers alike for her husband's transgressions. Though I did not want my Elimelech to leave Israel yet here am I still suffering for his wrongdoing."

And Naomi was certain that the Lord had forsaken them forever. But Ruth would not be downcast and, having finished the grinding, she stood and looked down from the neglected land of Elimelech upon the rich fertile farms in the valley below, where the morning breeze stirred the shimmering green and yellow fields of young corn and wheat and ripe barley. And there rose up to them the crowing of cocks from the barnyards, the lowing of cattle, the bark of dogs, the braying of donkeys, and the shouts of men reaping the barley harvest, swinging their sickles of flint and gathering the grain into sheaves. And Ruth observed how women went after the harvesters, gleaning the fallen grain and reaping the corners of the fields which the men left uncut. "Are those the bondwomen of the master of the field?" she asked of Naomi.

"No," said Naomi. "It is a law among us, which Moses brought down from Mount Sinai, that the owner of the harvest may not take the gleanings thereof for himself. The law says: *And when ye reap the harvest of your land, thou shalt not wholly reap the corners of thy field, neither shalt thou gather the gleaning of thy harvest; thou shalt leave them for the poor, and for the stranger.*"

Ruth said: "It is indeed a good and bountiful God whose law it is that men must provide for those among them who have not."

And Naomi said: "Indeed our law says further: *When thou reapest thine harvest in thy field, and hast forgot a sheaf in the field, thou shalt not go again to fetch it: it shall be for the stranger, for the fatherless, and for the widow: that the Lord Thy God may bless thee in all the work of thine hands. And when thou beatest thine olive tree, thou shalt not go over the boughs again: it shall be for the stranger, for the fatherless, and for the widow. And when thou gatherest the grapes of thy vineyard, thou shalt not glean it after thee: it shall be for the stranger, the fatherless, and the widow.*"

"And am I not all of these," said Ruth, "a stranger, fatherless, and a widow? So shall I go gleaning and shall bring barley that we may eat and thrive here, Naomi."

"But it is not seemly," said Naomi sharply, "for a woman of the family of Elimelech to go gleaning in the fields, else would I myself have gone down. And the men in the field may molest you."

Ruth said: "But didst thou not tell me that they think better of women than do the men of Moab?"

And Naomi said: "Perhaps I should have told you also that the difference between men lies less in what they do than in what they think. And besides, did you not hear what Tobias said? The women of Bethlehem will speak ill of you."

"Let them speak," said Ruth, her dark eyes flashing. "They can say no worse of me than they now think." And Ruth said: "Let me now go down to the fields and glean after him in whose sight I shall find favor."

Naomi smiled then and said: "Sometimes it seems to me that you are not my daughter-in-law but the true daughter of my flesh and my spirit." And she kissed Ruth and said: "Go, my daughter," and gave her a large apron in which to gather the barley and pointed out to her the richest of the fields in the valley below. "Go there, my daughter," she said.

So Ruth got up on her milk-white donkey and rode down to the valley and went to that field which Naomi had shown her. And it happened to be one of the fields of Boaz; for cool-eyed Elias, who watched over his men, was standing within the entrance to the field, wearing the ram's horn at his belt with which he summoned the men. And Ruth got down from her donkey and went over to Elias and was relieved to see in his austere face that this was the kind of man who would not molest a woman. And she said to him: "Let me glean, I pray thee, and gather after the reapers among thy sheaves."

But his look upon her was not friendly, and Elias said sternly: "You are the Moabitess, are you not?"

Ruth nodded her head, being too fearful to speak.

And he said: "Our law requires of us that we do not forbid the stranger to glean. This is not a matter of kindness but of justice. I must let you in. But I counsel you not to divert the men in the field. And you had best take off those Moabite amulets; and you had best veil your face."

So Ruth, seeing that otherwise he would not let her in, removed the golden amulets from her forehead and put them in the pocket of her dress; and she veiled her face with the end of her black headcloth and entered quickly into the field and took her place with the women gleaning after the harvesters.

And among the harvesters who went stripped to the waist and sweating in the sun she saw Gibbor the Benjamite, the mighty young man who had come to sit beside her at the Passover feast in the house of Tobias; and his powerful chest was as hairy as his hands, a red fell covered his flesh. But Gibbor did not see Ruth, for he was hard at work at the head of the men, reaping faster than all the rest though he laughed and made light of the labor. He led them in the singing of songs as they worked:

> Rise up, my love, my fair one,
> And come away.

The men sang together as they moved forward upon the standing grain, swinging their scythes:

> For, lo, the winter is past,
> The rain is over and gone;
> The flowers appear on the earth;
> The time of the singing of birds is come,
> And the voice of the turtle is heard in our land;
> The fig tree ripeneth her green figs,

89

And the vines are in blossom
They give forth their fragrance,
Arise my love
And come away.

And Ruth worked hard and steadily, bending in the hot sun to gather the fallen grain, and moving forward with the women after the men; and though the heat and the unaccustomed labor wearied her, though her arms and back ached, and the sun burnt her hands and the stubble cut her feet, she was happy and content as she saw the good barley heaped in her apron, for she persevered and gathered as much as the other, more practiced women.

They, for the most part, were older than Ruth, inured by time to the labor, burnt brown by the sun, and hardened by their unfortunate lot. Yet they spoke cheerfully to each other and chaffed the men whom they followed; and they too broke into song:

My beloved is white and ruddy,
Towering above ten thousand
His head is as the most fine gold,
His locks are curled and black as the raven.

And the men answered them singing:

Thou hast ravished my heart, my sister, my bride;
Thou hast ravished my heart with one look of thine eyes,

And again the women sang:

His eyes are like doves beside water brooks
Washed with milk and most fitly set,
His cheeks are as beds of spices, as banks of sweet herbs
His lips are like lilies flowing with myrrh.

And again the men answered:

How fair is thy love, my sister, my bride
How much better is thy love than wine,
Thy lips, O my bride, are as honeycomb
Honey and milk are under thy tongue.

Then one of the women working near by to Ruth and
seeing that she was a newcomer and had not joined in the
song, called to her saying: "You are a stranger here, are
you not?" And Ruth saw that the woman lacked one hand,
which had been hacked off at the wrist, though she gleaned
very dexterously nonetheless.

"I have just lately come up into Judah," said Ruth.

"But why do you veil your face?" asked the woman.
"Where are you from?"

And Ruth said hastily: "It is to keep my too tender
skin from the sun."

Then the other laughed harshly and said: "When you
have gleaned in the fields so long as I have you will cease
caring for your skin, and no part of you will be tender.
This is no place for the tender. You see this?" And she
raised up the stump of her arm. "My husband was fighting
another man harvesting in his field and my poor husband
was getting the worst of it so I went to his aid and took
hold of his adversary by the secret parts, which is against
our law. So they cut off my hand; though my husband died
of his wounds. Men put great store by their manhood.
You'd think it was something holy—the way they safeguard it, and they give the Lord God a tiny bit of it at
birth—when they are circumcised. It is their most precious
sacrifice." And she laughed aloud. "Anyway I am no longer
tender, I can tell you."

And it happened that Gibbor had stopped nearby them
to bind up a sheaf of grain and he heard the woman's
laughter and the last of her talk. And Gibbor called out

to the woman and said: "Do you not know, my little flower, why it is that you are no longer tender? It is because having no husband you lack for love, without which no woman remains tender."

And the woman answered him harshly: "I am no little flower; but you are a hairy bumble bee lighting wherever you can."

And Gibbor said: "It is because the sons of Benjamin are the sons of Rachel whom Jacob loved dearly that we are great lovers."

The woman said: "You are all alike whether sons of a son of Rachel whom Jacob loved or of Leah whom he did not love yet gave to her many sons. You are all alike wanting forever to display your precious manhood."

And Gibbor answered her, singing:

Thou hast ravished my heart, my sister, my bride;
Thou hast ravished my heart with one look of thine
*   eyes. . . .*

And the woman answered him: "Sing rather of what *you* have ravished, O wolf of Benjamin!"

And Gibbor sang:

How fair and pleasant art thou, O love, for delights!

And having finished binding the sheaf he approached the woman, still singing:

Come, my beloved, let us go forth into the field.

But the woman rose up from her gleaning and said: "I want none of your idle song of love when I am gathering good barley. Go back to your reaping, Gibbor." And the other women working nearby laughed and pointed at him and cried: "Go back to your reaping, you left-handed son of Benjamin, you shall reap no women today."

And Gibbor was about to turn away from the one-handed woman when his eyes lighted upon the bent figure nearby her. And he saw that this woman was young and new to the field. So he came close to her and went around to look upon her face, but it was darkly veiled.

And it happened that Elias, the foreman, was going across the field and he saw Gibbor among the women, so he blew a blast on his ram's horn and called to Gibbor to return to his work and Gibbor returned to his place at the head of the reapers. But he looked back again and again at the young figure of that silent veiled stranger until, seeing that she was gleaning alone between two of the sheaves and that Elias was gone to meet Boaz, who had come to the entrance to the field, Gibbor went over to her and stood before her and said: "Who are you?"

She looked up at him and said nothing; but he saw above the black veil those dark eyes which had drawn him to her at the table of Tobias. And Gibbor put out his hairy left hand and lifted the veil from her face. "You are the Moabite woman who came with Naomi," he said, his avid eyes lighting. "And I have heard of your springtime revelry in Moab, of how the women there go up to the high place and give themselves freely to the men."

Ruth stood up before him.

"Surely," said Gibbor, "you will not deny me a kiss or two." And he put his two red-haired hands upon her.

And Ruth let fall the grain she had gathered and retreated from before him until she came up against one of the sheaves; but Gibbor pressed close upon her there, holding her to his hairy chest in his powerful arms while she struggled against him.

And Gibbor was intent upon having his way with Ruth so that he did not perceive that Boaz had come into the field to look upon the work of his young men. Boaz was riding his roan stallion, Yohfe, and he greeted the men as he came, saying: "The Lord be with you!" and they answered him, saying: "The Lord bless you!" And Elias was walking beside his horse.

And Boaz as he approached heard the struggling of Ruth with Gibbor and came upon them between the sheaves. And Boaz reached down from his horse and took Gibbor by the scruff of the neck and flung him away from Ruth, who turned and bowed her head and stood weeping against the sheaf so that Boaz could not see her face.

And Boaz was very angry, saying: "You know well, Gibbor, that I will have no one forced in my fields."

And Gibbor was angry, too, saying: "There is no king in Israel, and every man does what is right in his own eyes."

And Boaz answered: "But none are slaves here; neither women nor men."

And they might have come to blows had not cool-eyed Elias put a restraining hand upon the arm of Gibbor and said: "Go back to your labor," and Gibbor turned away and went among the reapers. Then Elias took the head of Yohfe, the horse of Boaz, and drew him away, saying: "Come, Boaz, there are still the flocks in the pasture to be seen."

And Boaz went on with Elias a little way, leaving Ruth by the sheaf of grain; but his eyes were drawn back to that forlorn figure as he listened to Elias, who asked: "Shall I send Gibbor away? With women in the field he behaves like an ox."

Then Boaz smiling, said: "There is an old saying: *Where there are no oxen the crib is clean; but much is got from the vigor of the ox.*" And still looking back at that strange woman bending now to gather up the grain she had dropped, Boaz said: "It is not for me who am not lacking in lust to chastise Gibbor, who is not pleasing in the eyes of women and lacks a wife because of the curse our fathers put upon the sons of Benjamin."

Elias said: "Regardless of what Moses said, if I had my way women would not be let into the fields to glean, at least not while the men are working there. . . ." And he went on complaining of the trouble women made between men when they came in among them.

But Boaz was not listening to Elias. He reined in his horse, saying, "Wait, Yohfe; wait, my beauty." And he said to Elias, still looking backward: "Tell me, who is that young woman? Do I not know her?"

And Elias was loath to tell him: "It is Ruth, the strange woman that came with Naomi out of the country of Moab. She came down to the field and asked me to let her glean and she has been gleaning diligently since morning. It is time for the midday meal." And he raised the ram's horn to his lips and sounded a loud cheerful call, summoning the reapers to their food. And Elias said: "Let us go and eat, Boaz."

But Boaz gave no heed. "Ruth," he had heard, and was recalling how she had stood in the dark doorway of Tobias' house; and he wheeled his horse and left Elias and rode after Ruth who was walking away with her burden of grain. He called after her and she stood waiting until Yohfe came and halted nearby her. And Boaz said gently: "Do not go away to glean in another field. Stay here among the women and I shall see to it that no man molests you. And when you are thirsty go to the jars they have filled, and fear not."

Ruth dropped her dark veil as he spoke and she turned her tear-stained face up to Boaz, searching to see what had moved him toward her, but her eyelids fell before the strength of his manly gaze. "Why have I found grace in thy sight," she said softly, her words flowing slowly, "that thou shouldst take knowledge of me, seeing that I am a stranger?"

And Boaz said: "You did not observe me when you first arrived at the house of Tobias, my kinsman, but I observed you. And I heard what Naomi told of your loyalty to her, and how you left the land of your birth and came to live among us—a people strange to you." He looked upon her in silence, and then spoke again: "You are——" and he was about to put out his hand to touch her, but Boaz restrained himself and said: "You will be rewarded by the Lord God of Israel, under whose wing you have come to take refuge."

Then Ruth said, "Let me find grace in thy sight, Boaz, for thou hast comforted me, thou hast spoken kindly to me though I am not a woman of thy people."

And Elias sounded his horn again, summoning Boaz to the midday meal. But Boaz was loath now to leave Ruth. "Come, eat with us," he said; and he got down off his horse and led Yohfe after him, and Ruth went with him, followed by the envious eyes and knowing glances of the others, the less favored women who were eating there in the field.

"A well-matched pair," said the one-handed woman.

"A Moabitess!" said another and spat on the ground beside her.

"A woman for all that," said the one-handed one.

But Ruth was content to be going beside the tall and well-favored man whose bearing was at once gentle and strong, whose look was at once proud and kindly, whose speech was at once warm and wise. And then, looking up at Boaz and observing his grave gray eyes and the raven-black hair glinting red where it curled on his brow and beard, it seemed to Ruth that indeed Naomi was right about the men of Israel, for never had Ruth seen his like in Moab.

And as they walked together Boaz spoke of the goodness of God who had made the richness of his burgeoning fields. And when they came to the pasture where his flocks were grazing, he stopped to look upon the woolly sheep with their gamboling lambs and the long-haired goats with their skipping kids, and he recited the sage advice of his old father Salmon who had left him this land:

> *Be thou diligent to know the state of thy flocks,*
> > *and look well to thy herds;*
> *When the hay is mown, and the tender grass showeth*
> *itself,*
> > *and the herbs of the mountains are gathered in;*
> *The lambs will be for thy clothing,*
> > *and the goats the price for a field;*
> *And there will be goats' milk enough for thy food,*
> > *for the food of thy household,*
> *And maintenance for thy maidens. . . .*

And Ruth saw that Naomi had spoken truly: There were men in Israel who were indeed unlike the men of Moab. And Ruth felt for the first time that she was safe and secure in this strange land as she went beside Boaz toward the place where his men were gathered about the plentiful food which he had provided for them.

The men, Elias and Gibbor among them, were sitting in the shade of a wide-spreading terebinth, eating heartily of the heaps of goat's cheese and olives, and dried corn which they dipped in sour wine to soften it. Two younger lads, too restless to sit with their elders, came only to help themselves to handfuls of food and then went off to compete with each other in stone throwing, in jumping and climbing, shouting at their play as if repelling attackers. And those sitting under the tree spoke of the Moabite raiders who had come again across Jordan and burnt down another defenceless village to the north and laid waste its fields and taken its harvest of grain. This time the marauders had come farther into Judah, westward beyond Debir toward Enshemesh on the way to Jerusalem. The news of that raid had just come to Bethlehem. And the older men among the harvesters of Boaz told what they had heard their fathers tell of the old days when a good harvest in Judah would bring the marauding Midianites up from the south to plunder their crops and their cattle, coming into the land like locusts to destroy it, year after year, taking the grain that had been garnered and all the fat flocks, and leaving no sustenance, neither food, nor sheep, nor ox, nor ass. Then the frightened farmers fled before them to escape with their lives, leaving their homes to seek refuge in caves in the mountains or within the walled cities; until Gideon, the doughty farmer of Manasseh, weary of working all year to set a table for his enemies, gathered an army and with the help of the Lord God of Israel routed them again and again until they ceased coming. During these last years of famine the land had not been molested. But now, seeing all about them the rich harvest in the fields of Boaz, the tall standing grain and the fat sheaves they had gathered, his men considered the chance that their enemies, hearing of their abundant crops, might be moved this year to return to rob them of it.

"And not merely the Midianites," said one brawny old fellow. "This time the Philistines may come from the west;

and those Moabites who came across Jordan may be spying out the land for others of their tribe who, circling to the south of the Salt Sea, may join there with the Midianites to come up again upon us in great strength."

And cool-eyed Elias, eating sparsely of the food as was his wont, said: "Then let us be well prepared to protect ourselves. Let us have our arms always with us, by day and by night, each man his stout club, his sword or his spear, or his bow and arrow; and let us keep our scythes well sharpened so that they too may serve to defend us if we are attacked here in the fields. And two likely lads like you," he said to two youngsters who had come from their play to fill their mouths hastily, "should practice diligently, remembering that this is not just a game you are playing."

But the boys were not attentive to Elias; and one of them, seeing Boaz approaching with Ruth from afar, said: "Here comes Boaz with the woman Naomi brought back with her from Moab. I have seen her drawing water at our well. She is not hard to look upon."

And the other said: "She walks like a princess. And my mother says she is of the house of King Eglon whom Ehud the Benjamite took by surprise and slew in his summer house with a well-aimed stab in his big fat belly. Is that true, Gibbor? You are a Benjamite; you should know. And was not Ehud your great-grandfather, who went to Moab to kill King Eglon?"

Elias said hastily: "Do not start Gibbor telling that story now. We have heard it often enough."

But Gibbor only said: "It is possible that she is of the house of Eglon," as he sullenly watched Ruth approaching with Boaz.

And the lad said with a sigh: "It must be very pleasant

to lie with a princess; and I have heard it said that the women of Moab are taught every spring by their priests on the high place how to sport with the men. They must be well practiced."

And Gibbor said scornfully, "The Jebusite harlots of Jerusalem or even those in the market place up in Bethlehem are practiced enough for the likes of you lads."

Elias turned his cool eyes sternly upon Gibbor and the two lads and he said: "Have you forgotten or have you never heard how the men of Israel when they dwelt in Shittim committed whoredom with the daughters of Moab and the children of Israel were stricken with the plague so that twenty-four thousand died? And the Lord God of Israel told Moses to command the children of Israel to slay every man who had joined himself to the abominations of Baal-Peor. And Phinehas, grandson of Aaron the High Priest, took a spear and went after Zimri the Simeonite who had taken Cozbi a Midianite woman into his tent, and thrust them both through with his spear, the man through his back and the woman through her belly."

And the two lads were very frightened as they listened to Elias who continued to speak: "For the woman Cozbi had been sent by the Midianites to beguile the men of Israel to the worship of Baal-Peor with her wiles. And it is well to remember also how Delilah the Philistine woman served the Philistine princes in seeking out the weakness of Samson the strong man of Israel. For may not this woman of Moab have come here likewise to serve her people secretly?"

And the brawny old man spoke again: "Then let us send her away; and let us keep all strangers out of our land."

But Elias shook his head and answered him: "It is forbidden us by the laws of Moses to deny sustenance to the stranger who comes to sojourn among us, and though it seems a dangerous law, still it is in our Book of Remembrance and we must keep it; but that does not mean we must not be on guard against the stranger who may be a spy for one of our enemies."

Until then Gibbor the Benjamite maintained his sullen silence as he watched Ruth and Boaz coming across the field. But when they had come within earshot he turned to Elias and lifted up his voice saying: "A man need not join himself to Baal-Peor when he takes a strange woman; nor need he be as weak in his head as was Samson. And it is quite possible that the men of Moab are not waiting for the harvest but are raiding us now because they are angered that one of their women left Moab to come and sojourn in Judah." And as Ruth and Boaz came nearer Gibbor said, "And if I had my way, instead of going about armed and waiting for the men of Moab to come and attack us we would go first across Jordan and take them by surprise and destroy them and take all the women of Moab away for ourselves. And I am a son of Belial if I could not vanquish the Moabites with three hundred picked men of Judah as Gideon took thousands of the Midianites with his three hundred men of Manasseh, especially if we could get from Tobias the merchant some of the iron and brass he has found in his hills. We could make us stout spears and shields and perhaps even some chariots like the Egyptians. And I am a son of Belial if I would not take ten of the women of Moab for myself."

And Gibbor spoke loudly so that Boaz as he came near with Ruth could not but hear his boasting; and Boaz looked sternly upon Gibbor as he greeted the men, saying: "The Lord be with you," and they answered him saying,

"The Lord bless you." Then said Boaz to Gibbor: "We are a people of peace. And the Lord God of Israel has commanded us not to covet what is our neighbor's."

And Gibbor said: "It is all very well for you, Boaz, who can have any Israelite woman you wish, to speak of not coveting what is your neighbor's; but I am of the tribe of Benjamin who lack for women and whom no Israelite will give his daughter for wife. And as for our being a people of peace have we not killed many men in battle—thousands and tens of thousands?"

Boaz said: "It gives me no great pleasure, Gibbor, to remember the men I have slain in battle, nor the thousands Israel has destroyed of those who would have denied us our homeland or would have enslaved us or corrupted us with their abominations."

Then Gibbor was silent; and Boaz bade Ruth be seated beside him and he handed her food and drink and helped her to wine into which she might dip the corn, as if she were an honored guest and not one of the lowly gleaners, so that it was clear to his men, who could not but be entranced by the ripe beauty and sweetness of this strange woman, that she had found favor in the eyes of Boaz.

And this was observed with increasing resentment by hairy-handed Gibbor, who sat silently drinking much wine; and with uneasiness and concern for the beguilement of his friend by cool-eyed Elias, who drank no wine at all.

And Ruth, looking upon these men of Israel as she ate among them, saw that they were at once like the men of Moab in their lusty male strength and unlike them in that self-restraint of which Naomi had spoken. Even Gibbor the Benjamite now sat silently staring at her. And her heart as well as her eyes told her that, among them all,

Boaz was the best. Like Naomi's Elimelech, he was both vigorous and thoughtful; and yet she saw no sign that Boaz was divided in spirit as Naomi had said such a man was bound to be. In his way with his men it was clear that he could be firm like a master and kind like a father; and with her, the woman, he was both gentle and manly; and all these traits were but the parts of one thing, his goodness, it seemed to Ruth as she observed and listened to Boaz. And he was at one, thought Ruth, not only within himself but with his God and his men. Before he broke bread he blessed the Lord God of Israel for his bounty; and while eating heartily he praised his men for the excellence of their labors which had brought forth this bounty.

Whereupon Gibbor spoke up and said: "Now tell me, Boaz, why need you thank the Lord God of Israel for this bounty when you admit that it is we who by our labors have brought it forth from the earth? And why is our God greater than any other god if we still have to labor for his bounty?"

And Boaz answered him softly but firmly saying: "Moses said: *Man does not live by bread alone, but by everything that proceeds out of the mouth of the Lord does man live.* And our God," said Boaz, "is greater than any other god because he has revealed to us his laws in order that we may know good from evil and learn the way to a good and righteous life."

"And yet," said Elias, "we are told that the Lord forbid Adam under pain of death to eat of the tree of the knowledge of good and evil which grew in the garden of Eden."

Boaz said: "And man had he heeded that warning might have remained there forever in the ignorance of the beasts, innocent as a child. The choice was man's; and man, with

103

the help of woman," and he turned to Ruth and smiled upon her, "chose to partake of the knowledge of good and evil though he suffer and die for it; and since then some among us, and we are all sons of Adam and Eve, have persisted in seeking that knowledge, in striving to know our God—that knowledge which, though it has brought us suffering and death, is yet our life, as Moses has said."

"And yet," said Elias again, "we are told that after the flood when the sons of Noah and their generations who were of one language went to the land of Shinar and there built a high tower whose top might reach unto heaven, the Lord was fearful and jealous of them saying: *Now nothing will be withholden from them which they purpose to do;* and he confounded their language so that they understood not one another's speech and he scattered them abroad upon the face of the earth so that they left off building the tower to his heaven, which is called Babel to this day."

Ruth said: "That is indeed a strange story and perhaps it was told not as a thing which had truly happened but as a fable to account for the differences in the languages of men—such as the difference between the speech of the men of Egypt and of the men here in Canaan." And Boaz, looking upon her and listening to her slow sweet speech; nodded his head in agreement.

But Elias said sharply: "There are no fables in our Book of Remembrance, and though it may seem strange to a stranger it is God's truth to us."

And Gibbor said: "Indeed I once knew a camel driver who had been to the land of Shinar and he said he had seen all that was left of the tower and it was a monstrous heap of broken brick and stones lying every which way."

"But that was a long time ago," said Boaz, "and since

then the Lord has manifested himself to our forefathers, Abraham, Isaac and Jacob, and revealed his laws to us, the children of Israel, and commanded us to learn his laws, through Moses his prophet who brought us to this promised land." And Boaz looked with contentment upon the fertile fields about him, peaceful and soundless under the noonday sun but for the song of birds, the whirring of crickets, and the shouts of the two young lads who, having stared their fill at the Moabite woman, had resumed their rock throwing and their climbing.

Then Ruth, who had finished eating and was satisfied, rose up to return to her gleaning. And Boaz looked into her dark eyes and said: "Do not fear to come and eat with us whenever you wish." And Ruth knew then in her heart that she loved this man, Boaz.

And when she had gone, Boaz said to his men: "I bid you not to molest this young woman who is a stranger among us. Let her glean after you in peace and put her not to shame."

Then said the brawny old man: "But have we not been warned against the Moabites? Did not Moses say: *An Ammonite and a Moabite shall not enter into the assembly of the Lord.* And is not this woman of Moab?"

Boaz answered: "It is not clear if Moses meant the women of Moab as well as the men. And did not Moses also instruct our fathers, more than once, not to mistreat the stranger among us? And this woman has said, when she left Moab with Naomi, that the Lord God of Israel would henceforth be her God."

And another man said: "But what if she told an untruth and is indeed come to spy out our land and our fine harvest for the men of Moab who have already made two raids upon us?"

Then Boaz said impatiently: "But you have only to look upon her——"

And cool-eyed Elias interrupted him saying: "As Samson looked upon Delilah—and to what end we all know."

Then Boaz smiled and said: "You, my friend, who remember Samson so well, do look with fear and without favor upon all women, whether strange or not." Whereupon the men laughed heartily. Then Boaz continued: "Therefore I bid you, Elias, to look upon this woman with watchful suspicion lest she be a spy." And then he looked into the sullen eyes of Gibbor saying: "As for the rest of you, I bid you not to look upon her at all; but, remembering that three times we were commanded by Moses to leave our gleanings for the stranger sojourning among us, I bid you again to let her glean after you in peace. What is more, I bid you also as you reap to pull out some grain from your bundles and let it fall for her to glean, for she has old Naomi to provide for, and is not a practised gleaner."

Then as the men got up to go back to the fields, Gibbor, addressing himself to another said loudly: "And is it not wonderful to be the owner of a field, for then you can be generous to others and, at the same time, to yourself—even with something which someone else has found on your land. It is too bad that old Moses did not give us a law saying who may glean the women!"

The face of Boaz darkened with anger and he raised his hand as if to strike Gibbor; but Elias put out his hand and restrained him.

Then Boaz said: "It is said: *Every way of a man is right in his own eyes, but the Lord God weighs our hearts.* We have no king in Israel and every man does what is right in his own eyes; but we have the commandments of the Lord God of Israel which Moses brought down to us; and here in my fields I shall strive with all my heart, with all my soul, and with all my might to keep those commandments. For the Lord said of them: *This is your life*. Sometimes, as in this instance, it is indeed difficult to know what to do as between two commandments. And when in obeying the commandment you are endangering your lives, when you are giving freedom to one who may be your enemy, it is doubly difficult. Yet we were surrounded by enemies then, even as now, when Moses on the way to this land so often enjoined us in the name of the Lord God of Israel to care for the stranger in our midst; and surely valiant men should put justice to others before fear for themselves. Return now to your harvesting." And Elias blew a blast on his ram's horn.

And when Gibbor and the rest had gone back to the fields Elias said again to Boaz: "Shall I send Gibbor away?"

Boaz was silent and thoughtful a while before he answered: "No. It is not the fault of Gibbor that the men of Israel have sworn not to give their daughters to the sons of Benjamin; and Gibbor is a lusty fellow. Nor can I sit in judgment upon Gibbor because, to tell the truth, it is not without desire that I too have looked upon the Moabitess."

And cool-eyed Elias said: "Then send her out of your field, Boaz. You know the proverb: *The prudent man sees evil and keeps clear of it; the thoughtless go ahead and pay the penalty.* The Moabitess has already disturbed the peaceful friendliness of your life with your men. Send this strange woman away."

But Boaz laughed heartily saying: "Do not fear for me, my prudent friend. I am no callow youth, innocent in the ways of women. I am not being captivated. If I am kinder to this one it is only that she is my kin by marriage and a stranger in Israel—and are we, Israelites, not commanded to be good to the stranger in our midst, for we were strangers in——"

"I know, I know," cried Elias, impatiently. "I know that Moses even while the children of Israel wandered in the desert went so far as to say: *Thou shalt not abhor an Egyptian because thou wast a stranger in his land.* And between us, I will say frankly that I have never seen the wisdom of that commandment for us, living here surrounded by enemies on all sides—Philistines to the west, Ammonites to the north, Edomites and Midianites to the south, and Moabites to the east. And even in our midst we have the hateful Jebusites within the thick walls of Jerusalem. And I have still a terrible childhood memory of those strangers—the spies who came and let into our city by night the cruel hordes that laid waste our land, destroyed our home, slew my father and mother, and violated my sisters before my childish eyes so that to this day I cannot approach any woman with love. No, I have never understood why Moses said that because we were mistreated as strangers in Egypt we must not oppress the stranger amongst us—the stranger who may be a spy or may, like this woman of Moab, bring down upon us the vengeful wrath of the men of her land. A stranger is dangerous, I say; and a strange woman is doubly dangerous!" And cool-eyed Elias was pale with anger.

"I know," said Boaz gently, "that reason is on your side. And I, who have fought the Philistines more than once though I am a lover of peace, know very well how dangerous our enemies are. Yet is it not clear that Moses brought us up out of Egypt so that we might not be as the corrupt and evil Egyptians but a people apart, serving the one God of justice, not with cruelty but with love and compassion. I do not mean, Elias, that we Israelites shall not be on our guard against treachery—and even against enchantment."

"Then," said Elias, "if she should indeed prove to be a spy, intent upon betraying us to her hateful people or corrupting our men to their gods and their ways, would you then have the Moabitess stoned at the Gate of the Judges?"

And Boaz said gravely: "I am a judge in Israel; and we have one law for all—stranger and homeborn alike. A spy should be stoned." And then Boaz smiled gently upon Elias: "You need have no fear, my friend. I shall not do myself what I have forbidden Gibbor the Benjamite. I shall restrain myself, as I have restrained him. I shall not go near the woman of Moab."

And when Elias had left him Boaz went to his handsome stallion and stroked its smooth coppery flanks, saying: "Count yourself lucky, Yohfe, my beauty, that you are a beast and not a man. When you see a likely young mare you are not plagued by doubts, are you?" And Boaz mounted upon his horse and rode off.

Having beaten out her gleanings of that day and got a good measure of barley—not unremarked by the other less-favored gleaners—Ruth, weary but content, rode happily up the hill to Bethlehem toward evening; and having tethered her milk-white donkey outside the broken door she went into the house and showed Naomi how well she had done in her gleaning.

Naomi marveled that she could have gathered so much the first day and took some of the grain for their evening meal, asking where had she gleaned.

And as Naomi prepared the food, Ruth sat down to

weave at the loom and told how she had gone into the field Naomi had pointed out to her—and it happened to be the field of Boaz.

And Naomi did not look surprised though she said: "Was it indeed," and she asked Ruth why she was no longer wearing her golden amulets. And Ruth told her of her meeting with Elias at the entrance to the field of Boaz. Then Naomi asked Ruth how she had fared in the field of Boaz. And she got from Ruth the tale of how Boaz had saved her from Gibbor the Benjamite, and of the generosity of Boaz which accounted for the fullness of her gleaning that day. And Naomi said: "Blessed be he of the Lord, who has not left off his kindness. Boaz, like Tobias, being kin to my Elimelech is kinsman to us—he is of the house of Nahshon, a prince of Judah—a valiant and worthy young man and well made, as you have doubtless observed this time."

Naomi looked up from her cooking to glance at Ruth, whose face was bowed over the loom. And Ruth said softly: "I have never seen his like in Moab—a man both gentle and vigorous, thoughtful yet strong in action."

Naomi said: "I knew his mother; we were near neighbors. I remember when he was born and how pleased his mother was."

And Ruth said: "Was he her first-born son?"

And Naomi said: "No. Her first-born had died. Hence he was her eldest son, though not the first-born. And his mother asked me about a name for him and we agreed on Boaz, meaning, *in him is strength.*"

And Ruth said: "As he spoke to me I was minded of what thou didst tell me of the riddle of Samson and the lion: *Out of the strong came forth sweetness.*"

Naomi looked shrewdly at Ruth, whose face was still

bowed over the loom; and it seemed to Naomi that the appearance of Ruth's face had changed; and she saw then that it was because Ruth had not put again on her brow the golden amulets of Ashtar. And Naomi was pleased, but said nothing about it and she waited for Ruth to speak.

But Ruth said nothing more. Then Naomi said: "Boaz is wealthy, too. So that it is good that you go gleaning in his rich fields. But this I must tell you now, my daughter: though it is indeed true, as I said to you on the way here from Moab, that the men of Judah are better than the men of Moab in the way they consider their women, and especially the old women, nevertheless when young they are as lustful as any Moabite and as prone to frolic in the fields with any maiden who will let them."

Ruth said: "There were among the women gleaning in the field some who do not think as well as you do of the way the men of Israel consider their women. There was one who had her hand cut off for what she had done in trying to help her husband in a fight; and there was also the wife of Zvuv who complained bitterly of how he went about prophesying and left her to labor in the fields to find food for their children. Being the wife of a prophet must indeed be trying; but it appears that the young Israelites when they are lustful like Gibbor behave no differently from any young Moabite."

Then Naomi hastened to say: "But you must not judge all the Israelites by Gibbor, who is a Benjamite and came here because women are lacking among his tribe, and the Benjamites have a bad reputation among the Israelites for their way with women. No man will give his daughter to a Benjamite. But as lustful as the men of Israel may be, at least they do not say their God bids them be wanton with women, nor do they make of their lustfulness an open abomination before their God; for the Lord God of Israel, though he commanded them to be fruitful and multiply, has also commanded them against the violation of virgins and the taking of other men's wives."

And Naomi came from her cooking to help Ruth untangle the threads of her weaving which had gone astray. Then she continued, saying: "Now you, my child, are a widow and a stranger; and men, as I have told you, are apt to forget their precepts in the face of their desires. A lusty man of Judah, even one less unrestrained by nature than Gibbor the Benjamite, may, on occasion, feel that these commandments do not apply to you. So, though I am pleased that you have found favor in the eyes of Boaz, and though I bid you go on gleaning in his fields, it is not merely because you are safer there than elsewhere. For I do not look forward to your gleaning endlessly, even there, harvest after harvest and year after year, burnt by the sun and bent with toil until you are like those poor worn-out creatures who have to glean in the fields like that one-handed widow and the fretful wife of Zvuv."

Ruth looked up from the loom, her dark eyes dream filled, and she said: "And what is it thou seest for me in the future, Naomi?"

And Naomi, as she brought the steaming bowl to the table, said: "I see you married to a valiant young man, well made and wealthy. I know, you have said that you would not want a levirate marriage; so I have done nothing about that, especially as Elimelech's brothers are dead and have left no sons. But for any other marriage you will need a dowry, at least to clothe yourself fittingly and provide yourself with those things which a woman brings to her household. And unfortunately, men being unreasonable creatures, the richer a man is the more dowry he usually requires with his wife, although you would think it should be the other way around."

Then Ruth rose from the loom and went to the broken door and looked out. She could see the green fertile fields of Boaz in the valley below, and eastward beyond the Salt Sea the long line of the high plains of Moab, and she said, "Dost thou think I have already forgotten Mahlon? And even if I would take another man in his place, dost thou think that any man here would have me, a Moabitess, for his wife, even with a dowry? And even if there were such a man," she said, turning to look around her at their poor home, "where is this dowry of mine to come from?" And Ruth returned to the open door.

Then Naomi said: "Leave that to me." And when she saw that Ruth remained standing at the door, Naomi said: "Come now, my daughter, and eat." And she took up her spinning whorl and her old eyes were smiling as she began spinning a strong new thread while Ruth ate of the food that she had prepared.

IN THE MORNING, when Ruth had gone down to glean, Naomi went to the gates of Bethlehem, seeking her rich kinsman, Tobias. For all of Bethlehem passed by the city gates in the course of the day.

There within the thick wall, in the open space between its two great gates, was the market place, where the merchants came to trade with each other, and the men and the matrons and maidens of Bethlehem came to purchase their needs and their wants in the booths of the artisans, the workers in leather, the potters, the silversmiths, and the sellers of food and raiment, of perfumes and jewels, of rugs and silks, of cotton from Egypt and of wool from the flocks in the fields beyond those two massive gates of cedar, wide open now to the constant stream of laden camels and donkeys coming and going.

And this was not merely the market place but the court of justice and of entertainment. For in the shade of the square stone tower of the right-hand gate sat one or more of the three judges of Bethlehem holding court for those who had grievances to adjust or agreements to transact. And in the vicinity of the round brick tower of the left-hand gate were the wineshops for the men and the sweet-shops for the women and the striped tents and booths of the wandering tricksters and clowns, strange wizards and soothsayers, who strove to beguile and amuse the passersby with their antics, their music, and their wiles.

And a constant noise rose up from the multitude of men and women walking and riding about that sunny dusty place, and from the children at play darting with shrill cries among them. But above all the hubbub rose the harsh angry voice of Zvuv who stood in the midst of the ceaseless traffic, now here, now there, exhorting the busy throng. And as Naomi went about seeking her kinsman Tobias in the crowd she heard the voice of Zvuv crying: "Woe to the children of Israel for their backsliding, for their forgetfulness of the commandments of the Lord God of Israel. . . ."

But Tobias was nowhere to be seen; and Naomi thought of going to find him at his house. But remembering the manner in which she had left him on the night of her arrival in Bethlehem, the old woman was too proud to return there. So she went on, inquiring after him among the merchants in the market, but no one had yet seen Tobias that day at the city gates. Still, Naomi knew she was bound to meet him there if she but waited long enough.

And the sun being warm she went to wait in the cool shade of the square stone tower of the Gate of the Judges, where the eldest of the three judges of Bethlehem, a venerable old man, a hero of Jephthah's war against the Ammonites, now half blind and hard of hearing, sat alone on the long judges' bench disposing quickly, one after another, of the less difficult cases which came to be dealt with early in the day. And he was attended by the scribe who sat nearby him with the great parchment scroll of the Book of Remembrance and a heap of inscribed tablets of dried clay, from among which, when instructed by the judge, he would draw the suitable one and read aloud the law of Moses for the matter in hand:

If thou lend money to any of my people with thee that is poor, the scribe was reading, *thou shalt not be to him as a creditor; neither shall ye lay upon him usury. If thou at all take thy neighbor's garment to pledge, thou shalt restore it to him by that the sun goeth down: for that is his only covering, it is his garment for his skin: wherein shall he sleep? And it shall come to pass, when he crieth unto me, that I will hear; for I am gracious.*

The aged judge looked sternly upon one of the litigants, a fat, prosperous-looking man, who still held in his hand the cloak of the ragged little man who stood shivering in the shade beside him. "Give him his garment," said the judge; and he turned to the elders of the city who sat in a row in the forefront of the small crowd of passersby, who stopped, as they came and went about their marketing, to listen to the proceedings. And the elders stroked their gray beards and nodded their approval of the judgment.

"But he still has my money," said the fat man angrily.

"You have heard the law of Moses as the Lord God of Israel gave it to him," said the judge and turned his watery old eyes toward the next litigants.

"It is an evil law," said the angry man; but he tossed the poor man his cloak as they made way for the next pair —two farmers, one of whom was leading a limping ox.

And this one shouted up to the judge: "The leg of my ox was broken while working for my neighbor and now he refuses to pay for the hurt to my beast which can no longer pull as he used to."

"Were you with the beast when his leg was broken?" asked the judge.

"Indeed I was with it," shouted the owner of the ox,

"for it is a very valuable beast and I would not entrust it alone to any man."

"Read him the law," said the judge to the scribe; "you will find it in the second part of the Book of Remembrance." And the scribe, who had been searching among his tablets, unwound the great scroll until he found the place and read:

And if a man borrow aught from his neighbor, and if it be hurt, or die, the owner thereof not being with it, he shall surely make restitution. If the owner thereof be with it, he shall not make it good: If it be an hired thing, it came for its hire.

"You have only to pay for its hire," said the judge to the second farmer; and, waving the two away, he motioned to the next three who stood waiting, a stout red-faced man, a young girl, and a youth, to come near.

And at once the father began speaking irately of the outrage done to his daughter; but the judge silenced him with a weary gesture of one bony white hand, saying, "I know, I know well what has happened," and he turned to the youth: "Now what have you to say?"

And the lad spoke, but so softly that the aged judge could not hear. He cupped his hand to his ear and said: "Speak up, speak up! Surely you were not so shy with the maiden or you would not now be here;" and loud laughter broke from the large crowd of passersby which had suddenly gathered.

Then the youth raised up his voice and said: "I did indeed lie with her but I love her and——"

"Was she a virgin?" asked the judge.

But before the youth could answer him the father shouted: "Indeed she was a virgin and he shall pay the price of a virgin!"

"You know nothing about this," said the judge. "Be still." And he turned to the daughter: "Were you a virgin?" And the girl nodded yes.

"And I want her for my wife," cried the youth, "but——"

"But I will not have that son of Belial for my son-in-law," shouted the father, "and he shall pay the price——"

Then the judge silenced them both with his white hands upraised. "Read them the law of Moses," he said to the scribe, who had unrolled the scroll to the place. And the scribe read:

And if a man entice a virgin that is not betrothed, and lie with her, he shall surely pay a dowry for her to be his wife. If her father utterly refuse to give her unto him, he shall pay money according to the dowry of virgins.

"You will have to pay," the judge said to the downcast youth; and seeing that no more litigants awaited his judgment he rose up from the bench, though he saw Zvuv come pushing through the crowd crying, "I have a complaint! I have a complaint!"

"And what is your complaint, Zvuv?" the aged judge asked; but the elders and half of the crowd went away.

And Zvuv shouted, "There is a sorcerer at the Gate of the Wineshops, and he professes to be able to perform all the miracles of Moses!"

"A sorcerer?" asked the judge. "Have we any law regarding a sorcerer?" he asked of the scribe.

And the scribe, after searching the scroll and shuffling the tablets, took up a small one and read: *Thou shalt not suffer a sorceress to live.*

"Ah," said the old judge, "a sorcer*ess*! But we have nothing about a sorcerer, have we! and the scribe shook his head. "You see, Zvuv, we have no law against a sorcerer.

Now if it were a sorceress——" He waved his bony hands wearily and left the bench.

And Zvuv cried after him harshly, "When Joshua, the son of Nun who brought the children of Israel into Canaan, had died, the Lord raised them up judges to judge them; and now their judges need judging. . . ."

But the venerable judge hurried off, the scribe rolled up the scroll and gathered up the tablets, and the remainder of the heedless crowd melted away from Zvuv, but for Naomi who, since Tobias had not yet appeared, remained standing there beside him.

And when Zvuv ceased speaking she said to him: "It might help matters if a woman judged again in Israel; then would a sorcerer fare no better than a sorceress."

But Zvuv only gave her a look of disdain and turned and went across the crowded market place toward the Gate of the Wineshops. And Naomi went after him, still seeking Tobias who was nowhere to be seen.

Nor was he among the many men idling and drinking there outside the wineshops listening to the music of a harp and a lute, a tabret and a pipe, while watching the black-robed sorcerer who was boasting that he could perform all the miracles of Moses save only the division of the Red Sea. And to prove it he poured pure water into an empty jar; and then having waved a wand and said certain mystical words he emptied the jar out onto the ground, making a bright bloody stain there, saying: "Thus did Moses change the waters of Egypt to blood!" And the drinkers were tossing him pieces of silver and demanding that he change his wand to a snake, when Zvuv approached him crying: "Begone, you slanderer of Moses, with your sleight of hand!" And Zvuv upset the jar, revealing the powdered herbs concealed therein with which the trick had been done. The sorcerer hastened to gather up the silver and he hurried away from before the anger of Zvuv, who then turned upon the drinkers in the wineshops crying: "Woe unto them that rise up early in the morning to take strong drink; and that tarry late into the night till the wine inflame them, and listen to the harp and the lute, the tabret and the pipe, but regard not the work of the Lord. Such a people will go into captivity; their enemies will come upon them, as it has been with the children of Israel again and again in times past, when their back-sliding has brought upon them first Edom, and then Moab, and then the Philistines, and then the Canaanites, and then the Midianites, and then the Ammonites, and then again the Philistines, and now have we not had word again of marauders from Moab. . ."

But none of the drinkers gave him any heed, for they were watching a passing harlot who wore tinkling silver bells on her ankles. Her eyelids were dark and heavy with kohl, and her perfume burdened the air where she went. And the young men among the drinkers began singing to her:

> *I've come into my garden,*
> *My sister, my bride:*
> *I have gathered my spice with my myrrh;*
> *I have eaten my honey with my honeycomb;*
> *I have drunk my wine with my milk:*
> *So eat, O my friends, and drink;*
> *Yea, let us drink deep of love!*

And Zvuv, enraged, shouted shameful words after the harlot, and he cried:

> *At every post will she sit down,*
> *And open her quiver for any arrow!*

And he turned again upon the singers, saying bitterly: "You do indeed hear, but understand not; and you do indeed see, but perceive not!"

And still the drinkers did not heed him and continued their singing:

> *Open to me,*
> *My sister, my love . . .*

And Naomi went to stand beside Zvuv and she said: "I have heard it said that the Lord kept the children of Israel wandering in the wilderness for forty years so that a new and better generation might come into this promised land. It is too bad that he did not keep them there longer. But what is the good of your great anger, Zvuv? Was not Moses himself the meekest of men, and did he not say, *My doctrine shall drop as the rain, my speech shall distil as the dew, as the small rain upon the tender grass, and as the showers upon the herb; for I will proclaim the word of the Lord!*"

Zvuv turned his burning eyes upon the old eyes of Naomi and said aloud so that all about them could hear: "Go your way, woman. Did not Moses cast down and break the tablets of the law in his great anger at sight of the children of Israel worshiping the golden calf? And what do you know of the sinfulness of the men of Israel today? Whoredom and wine take away their understanding. They turn from the Lord and go after Baal. They go up to the high place of the Jebusites in Jerusalem, and some make themselves high places here in the hills of Judah; they sacrifice upon the tops of the mountains and burn incense under the oaks and poplars and terebinths, and their daughters commit whoredom and adultery. Their women buy images of Ashtar and worship her in secret, bringing her offerings and burning incense before her. And see there

121

how they spend their days under the sun in self-indul-
gence!" And he spat three times toward the richly dressed
matrons and maidens, who crowded the sweetshops and
the perfume bazaars and stood waiting outside the booth
of two Ammonite crones who told them their fortunes
and sold them magic charms and small full-breasted figures of Ashtar with the serpent writhing upon her. And
Zvuv shouted at them: "Know you not, O women of Israel,
that unlike the gods of Ammon and Moab, the Lord God
of Israel is unchanging and unchangeable; that no magic
can move him; that only in his laws can you find the way
to life!"

But the women heeded him no more than did the men;
and the Ammonite crones cackled at him in derision and
whispered to the women: "This charm will bring you
love! And Ashtar will bring children to your house!"

Zvuv screamed: "Woe to such women! Moses said: *Ye
saw no manner of form on the day that the Lord spake
unto you in Horeb out of the midst of the fire, lest ye
corrupt yourselves and make you a graven image in the
form of any figure, the likeness of male or female.* And I
say, woe to you, women of Bethlehem!"

"And your wife, Zvuv," said Naomi standing beside him,
"what manner of woman is she now? I remember her as a
young maiden, gentle and virtuous."

Zvuv answered her angrily: "My wife is a contentious
woman. And three things are said of a contentious woman:
*It is better to dwell in a desert land than with a contentious
woman.* And again: *It is better to dwell alone in a corner
of a housetop than in a palace with a contentious woman.*
And finally: *A continual dripping on a rainy day and a
contentious woman are alike; he that would stop her stop-
peth the wind.*"

And Naomi said: "I thought so. And you, Zvuv, are a first-born son, are you not?"

Zvuv said: "It is indeed so. I am a first-born son. Like Sarah the beloved wife of Abraham and like Rachel the beloved wife of Jacob, my mother was long barren. Then she went to the tomb of Rachel and there prayed our Mother Rachel to intercede with the Lord for his bounty. And——"

"But," said Naomi, "if the Lord God of Israel is unchanging and unchangeable would the prayer of a woman or even the intercession of our Mother Rachel move him to open her womb?"

Zvuv said impatiently: "You know very well that barren women in Israel have done this ever since Rachel died in childbirth on the way to Bethlehem and was buried there by the roadside. And when I was born my mother dedicated me to the Lord. For the Lord said to Moses: *The first born of thy sons shalt thou give unto me."*

And Naomi looked upon the gaunt face and burning eyes of Zvuv and she said again: "I thought so." And when Zvuv asked why, she said: "Because you are so troubled. A first-born son with a contentious wife: what man could be more sorely troubled! And I have observed also that the wives of prophets are often either shrews or harlots."

Then Zvuv said in anger: "It is not my fault that my wife is a shrew. Were she a worthy woman she would take pride in my service to the Almighty."

And Naomi said: "I did not say it was your fault, though I thank the Lord it has not been my lot to be the wife of a prophet."

And Zvuv, looking into her wise old eyes, asked anxiously: "Can you then tell me, Naomi, what is it that ails my wife?—Why she who was once lovely and loveable is

123

now loveless—a harridan with a hateful heart—as vinegar to the teeth and as smoke to the eyes?"

Naomi said: "The sins of the fathers are doubtless visited not only on the sons but on the daughters, and through them on the sons-in-law also. And I remember well how rich Simeon, whose youngest daughter you married, was brought before my Elimelech in judgment for having gone up to the high place in Jerusalem when he went there to trade with the Jebusites until a sickness and a madness overcame him; and how it grieved my Elimelech that Simeon had to be stoned to death in the gate. And Elimelech sitting in judgment said then, I remember, that Moses, long suffering and patient as he was, even with his enemies, had been intolerant only of evil—which must be destroyed because it has the power to maintain itself alive to the third and the fourth generation. So may it not be that it is because of her father Simeon that your wife is a shrew; but that you, Zvuv, have turned in your distress and your discontent to the chastisement of your people? Not that they do not deserve and need it. But a contented husband, it seems to me, is not so likely to become a prophet."

Then Zvuv cried out: "But what can I do with her now? What can I do?"

And Naomi answered him pityingly: "You are so wise, Zvuv; you who know all the laws of Moses and the will of the Almighty. But you don't know how to deal with a willful woman. Surely not with prophetic anger, for is it not said: *An angry man stirreth up strife; and a wrathful man aboundeth in transgression.*"

And Zvuv said wrathfully: *Woe to the rebellious, saith the Lord, that take counsel but not of me; and that cover with a covering but not of my spirit, that they may add sin to sin.*

124

Naomi said: "That may well be true of you and your wife, Zvuv; but it seems to me that a man who does not know what ails his unhappy wife might have some difficulty discerning the will of his God. It is becoming the custom for some men in Israel to speak as if the Lord God of Israel spoke to and through them as he did with Moses. Now I have no love for the men of Moab or their gods which are abominable; but in all the ten years I lived in Moab I never heard a Moabite say he had spoken with his god!"

And Zvuv said impatiently: "Go your way, woman! What do you know of the nature of the Lord God of Israel, who speaks often to those who know him?"

Naomi said: "I have tried to know him as well as any man; but it is difficult to know anyone, whether man or god, who does not speak to you. And the Lord God of Israel has never spoken to me, nor to any woman since Eve so far as I know, except through men. To Eve, the mother of all men, he spoke only to chide her for wrong-doing and since then to none other; while, though men have been equally erring and sinful the Lord knows, he has continued to speak to them on occasion: to Abraham but not to Sarah; to Isaac but not to Rebekah; to Jacob but not to Rachel or Leah. And so we women, to whom God does not speak, have to do his will as best we can without such guidance."

Zvuv said: "You have the guidance of the men to whom God speaks."

And Naomi said: "Nevertheless, you men to whom God speaks and has given great wisdom are not always as right as you think. If, for example, Rebekah had listened to Isaac, wild Esau and not gentle Jacob would have been the father of Israel, would he not? And now it seems to me you are wrong in thinking that my Ruth, who left her land to live under the wing of the Lord God of Israel, would not make a good woman in Israel and——"

But Zvuv did not let her finish speaking. He spat on the ground and said: "*An Ammonite and a Moabite shall not enter into the congregation of the Lord.* Do you not fear the Lord?"

Naomi said: "Why should I only fear the Lord God of Israel? Has he not also said to us, *And thou shalt love the Lord thy God with all thy heart?* Is not the Lord God of Israel a lover of love, jealous of the love and the faithfulness of his people? And indeed I have loved him for his bounty, when he filled my life and gave me a good husband and sons to gladden my heart. But the Almighty has afflicted me—he destroyed my men for their wrongdoing and I am left bereft of husband and sons, alone but for the love and loyalty of Ruth the Moabitess who——"

But Zvuv, ignoring her pleading said aloud so that all within earshot might hear: *They that feared the Lord spake one with another; and the Lord hearkened and heard, and a Book of Remembrance was written before him, for them that feared the Lord, and that thought upon his name. And they shall be mine, says the Lord of Hosts, in the day that I do make, even a peculiar treasure.*

Naomi asked: "But until then, Zvuv, what until that day?"

And Zvuv looked impatiently upon her, saying: "Thus does my wife speak also, saying continually, 'But what now—what now?' It is no use talking to a woman!" And he turned away from Naomi and left her standing there, and went off shouting: *Behold the day cometh, it burneth as a furnace; and all the proud, and all that work in wickedness shall be stubble; and the day that cometh shall burn them up, saith the Lord of hosts. . . .*

And the Ammonite crones cackled and called to Naomi,

126

the one saying: "Why dost thou go after that sapless creature? He is no lover of women!" and the other: "Let us get thee a lusty man; anyone thou dost want. Thou hast only to name him and we will bring him here to thee with our dark powers."

Then Naomi laughed, saying: "Thank the Lord I no longer have need of a lusty man, though it is indeed a man I have come here to seek."

And the crone said: "It matters not to us if it be love or money thou dost want of a man. Come tell us his name. It will cost thee nothing if we fail to bring him."

And Naomi, jesting, said: "Then bring me Tobias the merchant."

And the crone called the other one to her and they took a brazier between them and boiled a brew over which they were mumbling an incantation when Tobias appeared, hastening across the market place toward the Gate of the Judges.

And Naomi called after him: "Tobias, Tobias!" But he would not stop until she ran and stood in his way saying: "I wish to speak to you."

Tobias looked upon her in ill-humor and said sourly: "It appeared to me when you left my house on the night of Passover that you would not be wanting to see me again. Surely you do not wish to speak to a mealymouthed hypocrite. Is it possible that you and your proud Moabitess need me after all?"

"It is about the property of Elimelech," Naomi said patiently. "I wish to sell——"

But Tobias brushed her aside saying: "I have no wish to buy your neglected property; and I have to appear now before the judges with seven of my workmen." And he hastened away and left Naomi standing alone.

"Thou didst not do very well with that one, didst thou,"

the old crones called to her. "Come let us get thee another. Try a younger man this time. How about that one over there, wouldst thou not like him?"

Naomi looked to where they were pointing and saw the tall figure of Boaz sitting upon his stallion that shone like burnished copper in the sun. And a merchant stood holding the horse's head and talked earnestly to Boaz, while the merchant's richly dressed wife and his daughter, their arms covered with jeweled bracelets, their fingers with rings, stood by, waiting expectantly.

And Naomi went to stand nearby them and she heard the merchant pleading: "But I will give you a herd of the finest cattle, Boaz, beside the three thousand shekels!"

Boaz said gently but firmly: "Nevertheless, the answer remains, no; and I must go now to sit in judgment." And he took the merchant's hand from his horse's head and said, "Let us go, Yohfe," and turned away toward the Gate of the Judges.

And Naomi went and stood in the way of the horse and spoke to Boaz saying: "You are Boaz, kinsman of Tobias, the merchant, are you not?"

And he halted the horse, saying: "I am he. And you are Naomi who returned to Judah out of Moab. What is it you want of me?"

She said: "Only a foolish woman would tell a man what she wants of him. Men being contrary creatures, the best a woman can do is to make it easy for a man to discover that for himself and to pray that it will please him to grant what she wishes."

And Boaz smiled as his handsome gray eyes gravely searched her withered face, and he said: "But why have you stopped me, Naomi?"

And she said: "It is to give thanks for your kindness to

Ruth the Moabitess who gleans in your fields and has brought me full measures of your good grain."

Boaz said: "It is not kindness I have done you or the Moabitess. Is it not commanded us that we provide for the widow and the stranger?" And he turned his horse from her and rode through the throng toward the Gate of the Judges, as fine a figure of a man as was to be seen in all that multitude.

And Naomi heard the merchant complaining loudly to his wife and daughter, who stood gazing enviously after the great catch that had got away from them: "He must want a fortune for a dowry!"

And Naomi said: "Had I a fortune I would gladly give it to him for a dowry."

"And for whom?" said the bitterly disappointed matron. "Would it be for the Moabitess you brought back with you?"

Naomi said: "Indeed, for my daughter, Ruth. And why not?"

"As if it were not hard enough as it is," shrilled the irate mother, "to get a good husband for the maidens of Bethlehem, you must bring one of those shameless strangers here who goes down to work in the fields as no delicately reared maiden would do and there catches the eyes of our men. We have heard how your Ruth has got herself into the good graces of Boaz, who feeds her and protects her from the other men and has them drop extra gleanings for her."

"Then," said Naomi, "why do you not take all those trappings off your delicately reared darling, those silks and jewels and perhaps even the paint off her face, and send her down to the fields also? Perhaps it will change her like my Ruth, who was a princess in Moab, into a sturdy and handsome young woman for whom a robust man might have some use. Perhaps your daughter will fare better down there."

"My Sara is not a Moabite wanton," screamed the enraged matron. "Do you think your Ruth is getting those favors from Boaz for nothing?"

Whereupon Naomi sprang upon her, pulled her bejeweled headdress awry, and would have torn her fine cloak from her back had not the merchant intervened and hustled his women away.

"Ha, ha!" cackled the two crones from their booth. "Thou art not having much luck today, old woman. Shall we get thee still another man?"

And Naomi cast them a scornful glance as she straightened her disordered attire.

"Then try again," they screamed, "the first one we got thee. An old man needs coaxing," screeched the one. "Especially when the woman is not young herself," squealed the other.

Naomi turned away from their cackling and returned to the Gate of the Judges.

There the three judges of Judah now sat on the bench together, attended by the scribe of the court. Boaz was in the middle, stalwart and thoughtful. The venerable judge, who had returned, sat on his right hand, and a burly blackbearded man sat on his left. Before the judges stood Tobias and two of the seven workmen who had come to ask judgment of their grievances against him. And behind the judges, perched like a gaunt raucous bird on the heap of stone missiles piled by the square stone gate tower, sat Zvuv, screaming his commentaries on the proceedings:

"And Moses said," Zvuv pointed his angry beak at Tobias: *Beware lest thou forget the Lord thy God in not keeping his commandments and his judgments and his statutes which I command thee this day; lest when thou hast eaten and art full, and hast built goodly houses and dwelt therein; and when thy herds and thy flocks multiply, and thy silver and thy gold is multiplied, then thine heart be lifted up, and thou forget the Lord thy God which brought thee forth out of the land of Egypt, out of the house of bondage; who led thee through the great and terrible wilderness, wherein were fiery serpents and scorpions, and thirsty ground where no water was; who brought thee forth water out of the flinty rock; who fed thee in the wilderness with manna which thy fathers knew not; that he might humble thee, and that he might prove thee, to do thee good in the end; lest thou say in thine heart, My power and the might of mine hand hath gotten me this wealth. . . .*

The scribe was trying to read from the scroll but could not make himself heard above Zvuv's harangue. And the black-bearded judge turned impatiently upon Zvuv crying: "Be quiet! *The rich and the poor, God made them both.*"

And Boaz said to Zvuv: "Let the judges judge here." And when Zvuv had ceased he said to the scribe: "Read the law. It is the fourth of the ten commandments."

The scribe read: *Remember the sabbath day, to keep it holy. Six days shalt thou labor, and do all thy work; but the seventh day is the sabbath of the Lord thy God: in it thou shalt not do any work; thou, nor thy son, nor thy daughter, thy manservant, nor thy maidservant, nor thy cattle, nor thy stranger that is within thy gates: For in six days the Lord made heaven and earth, the sea, and all that in them is, and rested the seventh day; wherefore the Lord blessed the sabbath day and hallowed it.*

Then Boaz said to Tobias: "Note well that the law says: *nor thy stranger that is within thy gates*. And your argument that these men, being Philistines, have never had any sabbath in their own land and expected none here is no excuse for you to disobey the commandment of the Lord God of Israel."

"But," said Tobias, "having these strangers to work for us on the sabbath makes it easier for us to keep the sabbath of the Lord. As when one of the judges," and here he looked first at the aged judge and then at the burly black-bearded one, "has wished to visit my house for a feast on the sabbath day it was possible for me to send these two Philistines with a litter for him and save him the labor of coming on foot."

And the black-bearded judge said hastily: "There is something in what Tobias has said about making it easier for us to observe——"

But Boaz turned from him to the aged judge who was having difficulty, even with his hand cupped to his ear, in hearing what was being said. And Boaz shouted to him: "Do you not agree with me that the law of the sabbath shall be strictly adhered to?"

"Yes, yes!" said the old judge. "Indeed, yes!"

"But," Tobias complained, "it is the law for Israelites and not for the Philistines."

Boaz said to Tobias: "We are told that even our ancient father Abraham said of the Lord that he is *the Judge of all the earth*. And the Lord God of Israel said unto Moses: *There shall be one statute for you and for the stranger that sojourneth with you; as ye are, so shall the stranger be before the Lord; one law and one ordinance shall be for you and for the stranger that sojourneth with you*. Is it not so?" he asked of the scribe.

The scribe looked up from the scroll of the Book of Remembrance and said: "It is indeed so; and he also said to Moses: *Ye shall have one manner of law, as well for the stranger as for the homeborn; for I am the Lord your God.*"

Then Boaz said to Tobias: "So, see to it, Tobias, that hereafter all your workmen, stranger as well as homeborn, can keep the sabbath day." And turning to the Philistine he said: "When you return to your land, tell your people how we in Israel deal with the stranger among us." And to the crowd gathered there he said: "In this way shall come to pass the promise of the Almighty to Israel in Jacob's dream when he said: *In your seed shall all the families of the earth be blessed.*"

The two Philistines then departed from before the judges and two of the five remaining workmen came forward, one of them loudly complaining that Tobias, having lent them their wages in advance because of their poverty, was charging them usury.

And when they had finished speaking their complaint, Boaz said to the scribe: "Read the law." And the scribe read from the scroll: *Thou shalt not lend upon usury to thy brother; usury of money, usury of victuals, usury of anything that is lent upon usury. Unto a foreigner thou mayest lend upon usury; but unto thy brother thou shalt not lend upon usury; that the Lord thy God may bless thee——*"

And Tobias cried out: "But one of these two is no Israelite. That one is from Ammon! Of him I may take usury. And is it not true also that the law which says we may not eat of the animal which dies of itself and is not slaughtered—that law says the meat may be given to the stranger to eat? So tell me, Boaz, where now is that one manner of law, as well for the stranger as for the home-born! And if you deny me the usury from the Ammonite I shall go to the High Priest of the Tabernacle at Shiloh and get justice there."

And Boaz looked perplexed and beckoned to the scribe to bring him the scroll, which he scrutinized and then passed to the eldest judge saying: "What is the reason for this?"

The old judge stroked his white beard and considered the passage and said: "He who lends to a foreigner runs the risk that the borrower may go and return to his land taking the loan with him. Hence is the lender permitted to ask usury of the foreigner."

"And that is just," said Boaz, returning the scroll to the scribe. "Hence, Tobias, you will return to the Israelite his usury. But the Ammonite must pay for his loan; unless he wishes to remain here and be circumcised and become as one of us."

Whereupon Zvuv from his rock pile began screaming again: "Moses said: *An Ammonite or a Moabite shall not enter into the congregation of the Lord; even to their tenth generation.*" And the frightened Ammonite did not tarry to consider the judgment of Boaz but went quickly away with the Israelite who had won his complaint.

And Naomi, who stood nearby the bench of the judges saw a look of distress in the grave gray eyes of Boaz which had fallen upon her.

Then the remaining three of Tobias' seven workmen, who had been squatting down on their haunches, stood up before the judges and complained that Tobias refused to pay them the wages he had promised, because the cargo of iron and brass which they had dug for him from his hills had been stolen from their caravan by the Moabite raiders.

Then Tobias said indignantly: "Having lost the value of the metal shall I also pay wages to these three who did not deliver it where they were sent?"

To which the three workmen replied that they had been promised their wages not for delivery of the metal but for the time spent in the service of Tobias, laboring in his mines and driving his camels.

The judges looked to the scribe, who searched among his tablets and in the scroll of the Book of Remembrance for a law to suit this case; and Tobias swore that he had promised the men wages only upon delivery of the iron and brass; and the men swore that Tobias lied.

And Zvuv screamed from his perch: *I will be a swift witness against the false swearers and against those that oppress the hireling in his wages and heed not my commandments, says the Lord of hosts* . . . and a great crowd of passersby gathered about the court to watch the outcome.

And Tobias was very angry and shouted at Zvuv: "Be still, you bird of prey!"

And Zvuv in a frenzy answered him: *There is a generation whose teeth are as swords, their great teeth as knives, to devour the poor from off the earth, and the needy from among men!*

And Tobias appealed to the judges, saying: "Shall I have no consideration because I am rich? You, my kinsman, Boaz, are also rich. And you," he cried to the black-bearded judge, "have not disdained to receive gifts from my riches; and you," he shouted to the aged one, "have gladly taken your ease in my litters and in my summer house in the hills; and——"

But the shrill voice of Zvuv drowned him out: "Moses said, *Judges and officers shalt thou make thee in all thy gates, which the Lord thy God giveth thee throughout thy tribes: and they shall judge the people with just judgment. Thou shalt not wrest judgment; thou shalt not respect persons; neither take a gift: for a gift doth blind the eyes of the wise and pervert the words of the righteous."*

And seeing the scribe motion to the judges that he could find no suitable law, Zvuv raised his birdlike beak and screamed to them: *Open your mouths, judge righteously and plead the cause of the poor and the needy!*

Then Boaz silenced him saying: "You need have no fear, Zvuv, that my kinship to Tobias will incline me in his favor; nor that his gifts will sway any of the judges; nor will we be swayed by the poverty of his workmen. For Moses said: *Neither shalt thou favor a poor man in his cause.* And again he said: *Thou shalt not respect the persons of the poor, nor honor the person of the mighty; but in righteousness shalt thou judge thy neighbor.* And Moses charged all the judges of Israel saying: *Hear the causes between your brethren, and judge righteously between a man and his brother, and the stranger that is with him. Ye shall not respect persons in judgment; ye shall hear the small and the great alike; ye shall not be afraid of the face of man, for the judgment is God's.* And now I bid you, Zvuv, to refrain from further comment, however just it may be, during our judgment." And Boaz turned for a judgment to the aged judge who quavered: "We must not oppress the poor to be sure, but on the other hand," and he faltered, casting a fearful glance at Tobias, "these workmen were responsible for the iron and brass entrusted to them and we must consider the loss Tobias has suffered already."

Then Boaz turned for a judgment to the black-bearded one who said very quickly: "As I have already said, *The rich and the poor, God made them both;* and the Lord God of Israel promised to us the fatness of this land—as Moses said: *this land whose stones are iron and out of whose hills thou mayest dig brass*—but were it not for Tobias who set these men to work on the hills of the land we should get no iron and brass from them. Therefore my judgment is for Tobias."

And Zvuv from his rock pile screamed again: *He that justifieth the wicked and he that condemneth the righteous, even they both are an abomination to the Lord!*

Then Boaz, having silenced him with a stern look, said to Tobias: "And where was this iron and brass being sent?"

And Tobias answered him: "To the Philistines, who offered me the best price for them."

Boaz said with indignation: "To the Philistines, the enemies of Israel who already have more weapons than we have and who would make of your iron and brass more spears and chariots with which to destroy us!"

And Tobias, incensed, cried out: "You who have just been so considerate of a Philistine would now deny me the right to trade with them. Where is your justice? Well, Boaz, there is no king in Israel, and every man does what is right in his own eyes!"

But a loud murmur against Tobias rose up from the elders and then from the crowd which had gathered before the court. And Boaz stood up from the bench and said: "It is said: *The poor man and the oppressor meet together; the Lord gives life to them both.* And have we not all one father? Has not one God created us? Why then do we deal treacherously every man against his brother, profaning the covenant of our fathers?"

And Tobias shouted: "But the middle one there is not my brother. He is a Jebusite; he came to sojourn here from

Jerusalem, where they sit on their walls and spit and throw stones upon us as we pass by on the road up to Shiloh and Lebanon. The other two will I pay the half of their hire; but that one will I pay nothing. And do not tell me now that there is one law for the stranger and the homeborn alike, for there is no law for this case, and in any case the law is not always the same."

And Boaz said: "Moses said of the Lord God of Israel: *He doth execute the judgment of the fatherless and the widow, and he loveth the stranger, in giving him food and raiment. Love ye therefore the stranger: for ye were strangers in the land of Egypt!*"

Then Tobias said in a sly voice: "We have heard, Boaz, that you are indeed a lover of the stranger, even of a Moabite stranger, and how generous you are to the stranger. But this—" and he pointed to the Jebusite—"this is no dark-eyed woman." And loud laughter rose up from the crowd.

And the eyes of Boaz fell again upon Naomi, who had gone to stand nearby Tobias; and she saw again the distress in the grave eyes of Boaz as he lifted his voice above the laughter of the crowd and said: "How shall it come to pass that *In your seed shall all the families of the earth be blessed* if you remember only that strangers have been hateful and hostile to you, and you do not welcome the stranger who comes to sojourn with you and to share with you the blessing of the Lord God of Israel?" The laughter of the crowd then ceased, and he said: "My judgment is that Tobias shall pay his three workmen their full promised hire—the stranger alike with the homeborn."

And the crowd cheered Boaz; and the other two judges, seeing that the people were with Boaz and against Tobias, agreed also to the judgment of Boaz. And Tobias, crestfallen, said: "I will pay them tomorrow." But Boaz said: "Pay them now, for Moses said: *The wages of a hired servant shall not abide with thee all night until morning.*" And Tobias reluctantly opened his purse and paid them the silver due them. Then Boaz and the other two judges rose up and left the bench and the crowd of passersby dispersed, leaving only the gray-bearded elders sighing and talking among themselves of how judgment in the gates had fallen upon evil days when the laws of Moses were no longer as clear as they used to be in the days when the elders were young.

Then Zvuv came down from the rock pile and Tobias went to him in great anger saying: "You have eaten and drunk at my table and slept in my house when your wife would not open your door to you; and yet you come here and speak against me before the judges!"

Zvuv said: "I am a prophet of the Lord God of Israel who said: *Remember ye the law of Moses, my servant, which I commanded unto him in Horeb for all Israel!*"

And Tobias said testily: "I could well do without prophets!" and he turned away from Zvuv in great ill humor and went toward the Gate of the Wineshops; and he would have gone into one of the shops but that Naomi, who had come close behind him, stood in his way. Tobias tried to brush the old woman briskly aside but Naomi stood steadfast before him saying: "You have lost many shekels, Tobias; but you can regain them and more if you will but take the great bargain I have come to give you."

Tobias asked: "What bargain?"

And Naomi said: "The property of Elimelech which I am offering for sale. True, it has been long neglected; but I shall let it go cheap for that reason. What can I, a poor woman, do with it? But with a bit of improvement in the hands of a shrewd man like you, Tobias, it will soon be as fertile as it was when Elimelech worked it, and worth twice again what you paid for it."

Tobias looked dubious, but he did not turn away from her.

And Naomi pleaded with him: "Just come and consider it, Tobias. That will cost you nothing."

And he saw her desperation; and Tobias the merchant knew very well that he could get a bargain from one who sorely wished to sell, especially from a woman. So he went with her to go out of the Gate of the Wineshops.

And as they passed by the booth of the Ammonite crones, the two called after Naomi: "Art thou not going to pay us?" "We got him for thee after all, did we not?"

And Naomi, to shut their shrill toothless mouths, tossed them a bit of silver.

Now Tobias was walking across the land of Elimelech, observing the fallen fences and terrace walls, the soil washed away by the rains, the weeds in the unkempt meadows, and the tangled vines and trees in the unpruned vineyard and orchard.

Tobias observed, too, how Ruth came riding her milk-white donkey up the hill from the fields of Boaz and, having tethered her donkey to a shady terebinth, came bearing so gracefully the burden of her gleaning, her lovely head held high, her shapely hips swinging as she moved through the fragrant air of spring, her feet gleaming white in the green flowery grasses. And Ruth was singing a song she had learned from the women gleaning in the field:

My beloved is white and ruddy,
  Towering above ten thousand;
His head is as the most fine gold,
  His locks are curled and black as the raven.
His eyes are like doves beside water-brooks,
  Washed with milk and most fitly set.
His cheeks are as beds of spices, as banks of sweet
    herbs;
His lips are like lilies, flowing with myrrh.
His hands are rods of gold, set with bright beryl;
  His body is polished ivory, overlain with sapphires.
His legs are pillars of marble, set in sockets of gold;
  His look is like Lebanon, upright as the cedars.
His mouth is most sweet.
Yea, he is altogether lovely.
This is my beloved——

Then, seeing Tobias, Ruth ceased her singing.

And long forgotten lust stirred in the ageing man as he caught the passing glance of her dark eyes. And he spoke to her saying: "Where have you gleaned so well?"

And she said: "In the field of Boaz."

And he said: "Is it not too hard labor for you?"

And she said: "Boaz has been kind to me;" and she went on by him.

And envy of Boaz who had bested him in the gate burned in the heart of Tobias as he stood and watched lovely Ruth go like a proud princess into the broken-down house of Naomi.

"And what is old Tobias doing out there?" asked Ruth as she poured out the grain from her apron.

Naomi, who was weaving at the loom, said: "He is looking at the land; he is considering buying it."

And Ruth said with delight: "Then we shall live well!

We will buy a good house in the town; and thou shalt have fine clothes and a servant and wilt rest from thy labors."

"Perhaps, some day it will be so," said Naomi, sending the shuttle swiftly back and forth in her weaving; "But I shall not spend this money for that."

And Ruth said: "Then what wilt thou do with it?"

"It will be for a dowry for you," said Naomi.

And Ruth smiled sadly: "Art thou still thinking of that?"

And Naomi said: "To be sure!"

Ruth said: "And may I ask of thee now to whom thou art going to give me with that dowry?"

"We shall see about that in due time," said Naomi. "First let us see how much of a dowry I can get out of old Tobias."

Ruth was silent a while as Naomi wove. Then Ruth said: "And what if I should not wish to marry the man thou canst get for me with thy dowry?"

And Naomi looked up from the loom saying: "But are you mad, my child? Surely you do not wish to spend the rest of your days like a slave in the fields, withering away into childless old age!"

Ruth said: "I would rather do that than bear children to a man whom I do not love."

"You are a foolish child!" cried Naomi impatiently. "My Mahlon is dead and gone; and even were he alive he could give you no child; and—and you will do as I tell you, for life has taught me much you have yet to learn."

And Ruth answered her gently: "Thou hast indeed taught me much, Naomi; and because of that I am no longer a child but a woman; and I will do only as my heart prompts me."

"Your heart, your heart!" mocked Naomi. "Your heart will only make you unhappier when I am dead and you are alone here with no man to cherish you."

Ruth said: "I would rather live alone than be cherished by another than the man whom I love."

Then Naomi looked sharply at Ruth saying: "Is there one here whom you love?"

And Ruth said softly: "But he hath not——" and she ceased speaking for Tobias had come to the door.

And Naomi said: "Well, Tobias, what will you give for the land?"

And he answered cautiously: "The land is in worse condition even than I had imagined. It is virtually worthless; and I could hardly pay you enough to make it worth your while; but I have in mind a plan whereby——" He glanced at Ruth and ceased speaking, and stood stroking his paunch.

Naomi said to Ruth: "Go get me a jar of water."

And Ruth said: "But we have two full jars, Naomi."

Naomi said: "Go get me another;" and Ruth took up a jar and went out, followed by the eyes of Tobias, whose lustful look was not unobserved by Naomi.

And she said: "Now what is this plan of yours?"

Tobias said: "You know that old levirate custom of ours which provides that the brother of a dead man marry his childless widow in order——"

"Indeed I know it," said Naomi, "but what has that to do with you?"

"Well," said Tobias, "since neither Elimelech nor Mahlon has left a living brother and I am the nearest kinsman——"

And Naomi said: "Are you indeed our nearest kinsman?"

"You know very well that I am," said Tobias. "And as the nearest kinsman is enjoined to redeem the property which a poor man sells it has occurred to me that rather than let the land of Elimelech be sold to another I might redeem this worthless property for you, even though you are not a man but a woman, and give you something for it—something more than it is worth—if Ruth went with it."

"Do you mean to say," said Naomi, "that you wish to marry Ruth!"

"But of course not!" said Tobias. "A levirate marriage is enjoined only on the brother of the dead, and I am not Mahlon's brother. Of course I would not marry a Moabitess! Was it not commanded us: *An Ammonite or a Moabite shall not enter into the congregation of the Lord!* But I would take her into my house and—" and he stroked his round paunch as he spoke "—and Ruth is a sturdy young woman who could make herself useful in my household."

And Naomi, watching the gleam in the eyes of Tobias, was prompted to say, "You old goat!" but she restrained herself; she bit her thin withered lips and held her tongue a while, and then said: "I shall speak to Ruth about it. But not while you are here. Go now."

And Tobias departed, stopping outside the door to watch Ruth come up from the well, balancing the tall black jar of water on her beautiful shoulder.

"And what did the old man want?" she asked Naomi as she set down the jar.

"He wanted you," said Naomi.

And Ruth exclaimed: "Thou wouldst not——!"

Naomi said drily: "No, I would not. But I would get from Tobias if I could, the dowry to get you the man you want. For *better is a dinner of herbs where love is, than a stalled ox and hatred therewith.* Now tell me my daughter, who is it that you love?"

Then Ruth went to Naomi and leaned her head on the old woman's breast. "It is Boaz," she whispered. "Oh tell

144

me, Naomi, is it evil of me? I thought never to love another. Nor have I forgotten gentle Mahlon. I did indeed love your son greatly; but this—this is different."

Naomi's face lit up; her old eyes beamed: "Indeed this is different, my daughter. And this is not evil but good. Have I not told you that the Lord God of Israel is a lover of love; and when he said it is not good for the man to live alone he meant woman also. So look back no more, my child, neither to Moab nor to Mahlon. Look forward now to life here in Israel and to Boaz, who would indeed be a helpmeet for you." And she kissed Ruth tenderly. "But he will come very high, my child. I have heard him turn down three thousand shekels and a herd of fine cattle."

And Ruth said: "But what good would a dowry do, even if I had more than three thousand shekels? He has not looked upon me since that first day in the field."

Naomi said: "I have yet to see a man, rich or poor, whose eye for a woman was not brightened by a dowry; that is, of course, if the woman herself has already found favor in his eyes. I shall keep at work upon our kinsman Tobias for the dowry—without his plan. Do you, meanwhile, do your best to catch the eye of Boaz again."

And Naomi, smiling, returned to her weaving.

But it was not easy to catch the eye of Boaz. Whenever Ruth saw him in the fields and moved toward him she would find watchful Elias in her way, hastening to lead her away to a place where there was better gleaning; and on the few occasions when Boaz, mounted on Yohfe, happened to come close to Ruth as he rode across the field and stopped nearby her with a look of entrancement in his grave gray eyes, cool-eyed Elias appeared as if from no-where and took Boaz away to show him something that wanted his attention.

And there were also women in the field who saw how the men while they refrained from molesting Ruth yet favored her by leaving behind them more grain where she gleaned and learned that Boaz had ordered it so, and there-after they watched Ruth jealously whenever he appeared, and made it difficult for her to approach him. And then when he had gone from the field without speaking to Ruth they would smile knowingly to each other and talk to each other, loud enough for her to hear, of how rich and valiant Boaz who could have any woman in Bethlehem was find-ing it difficult to choose a suitable wife. And the wife of Zvuv said bitterly: "For my part, I would advise no woman to marry Boaz, rich and valiant as he is; for there is too much thoughtfulness behind those gray eyes—there is too much of the prophet in him; and the Lord God of Israel protect any woman who has to live with one of his prophets."

Only the one-handed woman gave Ruth any comfort or courage. She said: "My man was no thoughtful prophet but a lusty fighter and see to what a pass he brought me," and she held up the sunburnt stump of her hand. "Thoughtful or lusty, prophet or farmer or fighter, any man is a trial to a woman. But since we are worse off with-out them, I say, get the best one you can. And this Boaz is a fine figure of a man who could give a woman great pleasure as well as much comfort. And were I as young and well favored as you, Ruth, I would go and stand before him, not when he is riding about in the field but when he is sitting still and cannot but look upon you."

So Ruth ventured to do as Boaz had told her—to go and

eat again the midday meal with the men, one day when Boaz was seated among them with cool-eyed Elias on his right hand and hairy-handed Gibbor on his left. And Boaz when she approached bid her sit and eat, but he was constrained in his manner toward her; and Elias looked coldly upon her. And Gibbor sat sullenly staring at her; until one of the two lads who were hurling stones at a tree nearby twitted Gibbor about his being a poor shot with a stone because he was left handed. Then Gibbor turned from looking at Ruth and answered the lad: "At the battle of Gibeah there were seven hundred chosen men of Benjamin—all left handed—every one could sling stones at a hairbreadth and not miss. And being left handed stood my great-grandfather Ehud the Benjamite in very good stead." Ruth knew then that Gibbor and Elias would try to discomfort her in the presence of Boaz but she was determined to remain there in his sight.

"In those days," said Gibbor, returning to Ruth, "the children of Israel served Eglon the king of Moab; and they sent a present by Ehud to King Eglon. I heard my grandfather tell of it many times as his father told it to him. Ehud made him a sword which had two edges of a cubit length; and he girded it under his raiment upon his right thigh, as I do my sword." And Gibbor lifted his raiment to show Ruth the sword upon his thick hairy thigh. "And my great-grandfather Ehud went and offered the present unto Eglon king of Moab. Now Eglon was a very fat man, and——"

There Boaz, angered by Gibbor's display of his private parts before Ruth, sharply interrupted Gibbor, saying: "I do not see how Ehud could have been your great-grandfather, for since his time we have had five great judges who were heroes in Israel: Shamgar who was also a Benjamite and routed the Philistines with an oxgoad, and Deborah, the woman, who got Barak to fight King Jabin of Canaan——"

And Ruth to divert and calm Boaz said: "And was it not then that Jael the Kenite woman killed Sisera the general of King Jabin with a tent pin?"

Boaz said: "Indeed it was; and a brave thing for a woman to do; and a thing for which we should be doubly grateful seeing that Jael was not a woman of Israel." And his words and his glance gladdened the heart of Ruth. Then Boaz turned again to Gibbor saying: "And after Deborah we had Gideon of Manasseh who routed the Midianite marauders and also the kings Zebah and Zalmuna. And then Jephthah, also of Manasseh, who went out and routed the Ammonites and had to sacrifice his daughter upon his return. And then——"

And Ruth said to Boaz: "But I thought that since Abraham no Israelite ever sacrificed a child!"

And Boaz said: "Jephthah had to: because he had vowed a vow to the Lord that if he delivered Ammon into his hand he would sacrifice whatsoever came forth first from his house upon his return, and it was his daughter, his only child, who came forth to meet him with timbrels and dances."

Ruth said: "It was a foolish vow, for surely the Lord God of Israel was not moved by that vow to give Jephthah victory over his enemies."

And Boaz said to her: "Indeed that is wisely said." And his admiration of her judgment was plain to be seen in the eyes of Boaz.

Then Elias said to Boaz: "And who judged after Jephthah?"

And Boaz turned from Ruth saying: "Then we had

mighty Samson who slew many Philistines before they brought him low."

"With the help of a strange woman," added Elias, glancing at Ruth.

And Boaz returned quickly to Gibbor saying: "So you see that Ehud could not have been your great-grandfather."

Gibbor said: "Whether Ehud was my great-grandfather or my great-great-great-great-grandfather is no matter. What matters is how he slew King Eglon of Moab." And he looked into the dark eyes of Ruth to see if his words had discomforted her, as indeed they had.

"We have all heard you tell that story more than once," said Boaz impatiently.

"But," said Gibbor, "Ruth who is a stranger among us has not heard me tell it." And he returned to her, saying: "And when Ehud had made an end of offering the present he sent away the people who bore it; but he himself turned back and said to the king, 'I have a secret errand unto thee, O king'—speaking in the ancient manner as you Moabites still do. And the king said to his court, 'Keep silence!' And all that stood by him went out. And Ehud came to him; and he was sitting by himself alone in his summer parlor. And Ehud said, 'I have a message from God unto thee.' And the king arose out of his seat. And Ehud put forth his left hand and took the sword from his right thigh," Gibbor showed with his own sword in his hairy hand how it was done, "and thrust it into his belly and the haft went in after the blade and the fat closed upon the blade, for he drew not the sword out of his belly; and it came out behind. Then Ehud went forth——"

"We have had enough of that tale," said Boaz sternly, seeing that Ruth was ill at ease.

"And it is possible," said Gibbor, "that Ruth being a

149

Moabitess of the house of Eglon has heard how Israel was thereafter delivered out of the hand of Moab."

Then Ruth said, with uplifted head though her heart was heavy in her breast: "I am indeed of the house of Eglon and have heard the story of Ehud; yet have I come to sojourn here among you, and to be a woman in Israel."

And Boaz looked kindly upon Ruth.

Whereupon cool-eyed Elias, fearful of her fascination, said: "But I don't think the women of Bethlehem look kindly upon your coming into the field of Boaz. The women of Bethlehem are much concerned for our Boaz." And he began amusing the men with his mimicry of one of the matrons of Bethlehem who were trying to inveigle Boaz, the great catch, for their marriageable daughters, angling for him whenever he came up to the town: "Dear Boaz," sighed Elias, "how you must want a home-cooked meal, living that crude life with those crude men in the fields! You must come and let me and my Sara make you a savory meal. Sara is such a good cook, and she would delight to do it for you—wouldn't you, Sara?"

And Boaz though he also laughed was ill at ease, because of Ruth, who sat with downcast eyes, not eating what he had set before her.

"And," Elias went on, "When the mother cannot get him for Sara the elder then Hannah the younger is permitted to fling herself at his head!"

And Gibbor said: "Baal take those women of Bethlehem! I would welcome a woman of Moab any time she would have me."

And while the men laughed aloud, Ruth rose up hastily and went and returned to the fields. And since Boaz could not chide Elias and the men for their laughter without confessing that this strange woman had found great favor in his eyes, Boaz kept silent.

But he asked Gibbor to stay with him when the others had finished eating and Elias blew his horn and led them back to the reaping. And when they had gone Boaz said to Gibbor: "You have no more molested the Moabitess in the field; but just now you vexed her with your talk of King Eglon. Moses said: *If a stranger sojourn with thee in your land, ye shall not do him wrong. But the stranger that dwelleth with you shall be unto you as the homeborn among you, and thou shalt love him as thyself.*"

And Gibbor laughingly said: "Why then when I wished to make love to her did you stop me, Boaz?"

And Boaz turned from him, saying sadly: "You are a man of little understanding."

Then Gibbor said: "I confess that I do not understand you, Boaz; for I thought when you forbid us to molest the Moabitess that you wanted her for yourself. But it appears now that you do not. You are like the dog in the manger that barks the other beasts away, though he himself has no use for the fodder."

Then Boaz said: "I am not asking you to understand me, Gibbor, since I find it difficult to understand myself in these times. All the same, my too lusty friend, I want you to keep away from that woman."

And Gibbor went from him with a shrug.

T<small>OWARD THE END</small> of the barley harvest—seven weeks after
the Passover—came the Feast of Weeks. And everyone who
could go then would make the pilgrimage up to Shiloh,
carrying the first fruits of the harvest to the tabernacle
there for the service of sacrifice and thanksgiving to the
Lord God of Israel.

"And we shall make two loaves of shewbread for the
altar," said Naomi to Ruth, who was working at the loom.
"It is a merry festival. All the young men and women go
up, not only from Bethlehem but from all of Judah and
the other tribes of Israel, and many marriages come of it
This is the time of year when men are most easily moved
to marriage. And this is your best chance to be seen and
considered by Boaz, all the way up to Shiloh. And if not by
Boaz, then by another. There are other valiant young
men in Israel."

"I will marry no other man," said Ruth without raising
her eyes from her weaving. "But what is the good of hi
looking upon me when I am so ill clad?"

And Naomi said: "You are more beautiful in your worn
garments than many another who goes clothed in fresh
spun silks; and if Boaz cannot see that then he is blinder
than most men."

"Nevertheless," said Ruth, "I wish that I had a new

dress." And she stopped her weaving and held up the end of the length of cloth she had made and stared at it saying: "Why not?" and stood up, holding it against her body, saying: "Why make more curtains for the windows?"

Naomi looked at Ruth and said: "Why, indeed?" And she brought her bronze shears and helped cut and fit the cloth upon Ruth's fair form. "And I will give you the golden earrings Elimelech gave me for our betrothal," said Naomi.

So they went with the throng riding northward along the sunny road to Shiloh, in the cavalcade of camels and donkeys headed by the standard bearing the lion of Judah, which set out from Bethlehem in the early morning, gaily garlanded with flowers and fruits and burdened with beasts of sacrifice and baskets of harvest grains.

Among the happy harvesters and their womenfolk singing songs of thanksgiving under the bright blue sky of the land of Israel rode Ruth, beautiful in her new raiment with the great hoops of gold shining at her ears. And tied to the saddle of her milk-white donkey Ruth bore proudly the two long plaited loaves of shewbread she and Naomi had baked of fine flour for the Lord God of Israel and enclosed in molds of clay lest they be marred on the journey up to the tabernacle.

But Naomi had not told Ruth that some women of Bethlehem had said they would not let the bread of the Moabitess be offered together with theirs, citing the injunction of Moses: *Neither from the hand of a foreigner shall ye offer the bread of your God, because their corruption is in them;* nor how Naomi had brought the

153

women before the judges in the city gate where Boaz had said: "Ruth the widow of Mahlon is not merely a foreigner; she is a stranger sojourning among us; and Moses also said: *If a stranger sojourn with you and will offer an offering of a sweet savour unto the Lord, as ye do so he shall do.*"

And Ruth riding among the maidens raised her sweet voice and sang with the rest:

> *Make a joyful noise to the Lord, all ye lands,*
> *Serve ye the Lord with gladness;*
> *Come unto his presence singing . . .*

Then Naomi, riding beside Ruth, drew her away from the others so that their garlanded donkeys rode as near as possible to the two horses on which Boaz and Elias rode, Boaz on Yohfe, his burnished-copper stallion, and Elias on his snow-white mare, followed by Gibbor on a camel so heavily laden with the grain and fatlings of Boaz and so slow moving in that multitude that Naomi, fortunately, could keep up with them. And though Elias whenever he saw Boaz looking upon the loveliness of Ruth would do his best to divert his friend or to find some reason to canter ahead of the throng with him, there was no doubt in Naomi's mind that she was succeeding in getting the entranced eyes of Boaz fixed upon Ruth as she rode and sang with the pilgrims:

> *Know ye the Lord he is God;*
> *It is he that made us, we are his;*
> *We are his people, the sheep of his pasture . . .*

But there were other eyes also upon Ruth: the irate eyes of the matrons of Bethlehem—among them that one who had quarrelled with Naomi at the city gates—and these saw how the simply adorned beauty of the Moabitess drew the avid eyes of the young men from their own daughters whom they had tricked out for this festive occasion when the young men looked about them thinking to choose wives from among the maidens.

And there were, too, the goatish eyes of Tobias, who trailed alongside Naomi, plaguing her in whispers to get Ruth to agree to his plan. For Naomi, for all the shrewdness of her talk with Tobias, had thus far failed to persuade him to purchase the land without giving him Ruth.

And now, on the way to Shiloh, Naomi tried again to get what she wanted of Tobias. She let Ruth ride ahead while she guided her dove-gray donkey alongside the laden camel of Tobias and patiently argued with him that Ruth, being a princess of Moab, where they did things differently, was not used to that kind of arrangement. "And it hurts her pride," said Naomi, "that you will not take her in levirate marriage though you are the nearest kinsman of Elimelech and Mahlon."

"Her pride!" said Tobias, "a Moabitess!"

"Yet," said Naomi, shrugging her bony shoulders, "she is a daughter of the house of King Eglon who ruled over Israel for eighteen years; and she cannot be bought like a slave, Tobias. Now if you will but buy the property first I can then say to Ruth: 'I have sold this land and our house to Tobias and he has bid us come into his household where we can rest in comfort.' And with the money you give me I can buy her fine clothing and jewels for her adornment which will surely please and persuade her, and should please you, too, Tobias," she added. "But first you must purchase the property; and at a price which will make my plan possible; and you had better do it soon, Tobias; for you can see very well for yourself how the young men are drawn to the beauty of Ruth."

And Tobias, looking ahead saw that Ruth's milk-white donkey was flanked by the mounts of several young men—including even his grandson, the lad Joel, who having just turned thirteen was making his first pilgrimage to Shiloh among the men of Israel. And their voices were raised in joyful song—Ruth's high sweet voice and Joel's broken half-childish one among the strong voices of the young men:

> *When Israel went forth out of Egypt,*
> *The house of Jacob from a strange people;*
> *Judah became his sanctuary,*
> *And Israel his dominion.*
> *The sea saw it, and fled;*
> *Jordan was driven back.*
> *The mountains skipped like rams,*
> *The little hills like lambs.*

Naomi said to Tobias: "See there between Joel and Ruth rides Naaman, your nephew, whose look is intent on Ruth. He is not too wise a young man but he is lusty and he can afford as well as you to pay for whatever he wants. And it seems to me that the eyes of our kinsman Boaz also rest upon Ruth—not without interest, Tobias. Indeed one might think him jealous of Naaman."

And Tobias saw how though his own daughter Reba rode close beside Boaz he gave her not a single one of his glances, which returned again and again to Ruth. Tobias the aging man could see very well indeed how the beauty of Ruth stirred men. But Tobias the shrewd merchant, when it came to giving up money, was very cautious. He never gave money without security; and where was his security with this strange and willful young woman? It was not Naomi's land that he wanted. "I will think it over," said

Tobias; and rode away from Naomi to ride beside his daughter Reba, to counsel her to go and ride with Ruth and thus to draw the eyes of Boaz upon herself.

In all that throng only Tobias was troubled. Disgruntled Gibbor, who in the presence of Boaz could only look with silent longing at the loveliness of Ruth, diverted himself with calling bold pleasantries to the other maidens. And even Zvuv, that angry man of God, who loped back and forth among the multitude on a bony but garlanded mule, busily examining the offerings of each of the pilgrims, stopped to join in the singing of the young men riding with Ruth:

> *What aileth thee, O sea, that thou fleest?*
> *Thou Jordan, that thou turnest back?*
> *Ye mountains, that ye skip like rams;*
> *Ye little hills, like lambs?*
>
> *Tremble, thou earth, at the presence of the Lord,*
> *At the presence of the God of Jacob;*
> *Which turned the rock into a pool of water,*
> *The flint into a fountain.*

Then Zvuv went to ride alongside Tobias and chided him for having brought a blemished he-goat as his offering to the sacrifice of firstling lambs and bullocks and rams. "If it were an offering to a prince of Ammon who might buy your iron and brass, Tobias, you would not give him that lame and scurvy creature," said Zvuv. "And surely the Lord God of Israel should have the best of your flocks, perfect males without blemish, especially as your he-goat is for a sin offering, and you have much to answer for," said Zvuv.

But troubled Tobias only looked down with scornful

impatience upon Zvuv; and Zvuv said: *"The sacrifice of the wicked is an abomination; how much more, when he bringeth it with the proceeds of wickedness;"* and he left Tobias to return hastily to the young men clustered about Ruth and Reba and the other maidens, whose mothers had also sent them to ride with Ruth. For the young men were singing lustily:

> *Come, my beloved, let us go forth into the field;*
> *Let us lodge in the villages.*
> *Let us rise up early to the vineyards;*
> *Let us see if the vine hath budded,*
> *And the tender grape appeared,*
> *And the pomegranate be in flower:*
>
> *There will I give thee my love.*
> *The mandrakes give forth fragrance,*
> *And at our doors are all manner of precious fruits,*
> *New and old,*
> *Which I have laid up for thee, O my beloved.*

And when the young men had ended this song Zvuv raised his voice and admonished them saying: "O sons of Israel, it is indeed said in the Book of Remembrance that at the Feast of Weeks thou shalt rejoice before the Lord thy God. But that ancient song you sing does not celebrate the carnal love of man for the flesh of woman which is intended only for the fruitfulness of all mankind; it celebrates the love of the Lord God of Israel for his chosen people to whom he said in Egypt: *Come, my beloved, let us go forth . . .*" And though the young men laughed unbelieving at this, Zvuv continued: "Then were you betrothed to the Lord; and at Sinai, where he made his covenant with you, were you married to him. And it is his laws and commandments which in your song are the *pre-*

cious fruits, new and old, which the Lord laid up for you, his beloved, at Sinai. And each year on the Passover do you celebrate your betrothal to the One God Almighty, and now at the Feast of Weeks do you go to celebrate your marriage to him and the harvest this marriage has given you. For the Lord God of Israel is wedded to none other than his people. Unlike other gods, unlike Baal-Peor who is married to Ashtar, our God has no wife. . . ."

And Naomi who had urged her donkey through the throng until it rode close beside Yohfe raised up her voice and said to Boaz: "It would appear that Zvuv envies the Lord God of Israel because he has no wife."

Boaz turned his grave gray eyes to Naomi and smiled upon her and said: "Any man who has suffered like Zvuv at the mouth of a carping contentious woman has reason to envy the freedom of the Almighty who has no wife."

And Naomi said: "It is not for mere man to envy the freedom of Almighty God, who in his infinite wisdom saw fit to give Eve unto Adam. And though God told Adam that a man shall leave his father and his mother, and shall cleave unto his wife, yet men when marriage hampers them will blame not God but women for the loss of their freedom. True it is that women want marriage so that they may bear and raise in peace the children men give them. But men need marriage too, Boaz, because they do not wish to share their women with others, except in harlotry, and because they want sons of their own loins for their help and inheritance. Thus men, who are ever divided in spirit, both fear and desire marriage, which while it robs them of some freedom does greatly enrich them."

And Boaz said, "But what if a man values his freedom more than the enrichment which marriage brings?"

"Then he is no man," said Naomi, "even though he be potent among women as a ram among ewes. For though freedom is a fine thing, he shows himself still a child who wants freedom from the consequences of his own desires, he is but a child who wants to take his fill of what is sweet, without restraint and without care for what comes of his doing."

"Yet," said Boaz, "though the Lord our God saw fit to give Adam a wife and has told us to be fruitful and multiply and has commanded us concerning everything else including the evil of adultery, yet nowhere has he said that every man must marry."

"True," said Naomi, "but the Lord loves a bridegroom; for did he not say to Moses: *When a man takes a wife he shall not go out with the armed host, nor shall he be charged with any business: he shall be free at home one year and shall cheer the wife he has taken.*"

"And like the Lord," said Boaz, smiling upon her, "you, too, love a bridegroom, Naomi."

"Indeed," said Naomi, "I do. For I believe as the old saying goes, that: *Whoso findeth a wife findeth great good and obtaineth the favor of the Lord.* But mind you—it must be a *good* wife. All marriages need not be like the marriage of poor Zvuv. For, as the old saying goes further, *happy is the husband of a good wife; the number of his days shall be twofold.*" And she turned her wise old eyes away from his.

And the grave gray eyes of Boaz followed the eyes of Naomi to where Ruth rode ahead of them, radiant in beauty and happy in the homage which the young men paid to her beauty, for they said she was more beautiful even than the maidens of Shiloh who were famous for their beauty in all Israel. And Naomi returned her eyes to the thoughtful face of Boaz and said softly: "There is also an old saying, Boaz: *Better is open rebuke than love that is hidden.*"

And Boaz, with his eyes still fixed upon Ruth was about to answer Naomi, when Elias rode his white mare between them, saying to Boaz: "We are told that Moses said: *Three times in the year shall thy males appear before the Lord:* in the feast of unleavened bread, and in this feast of weeks, and in the feast of tabernacles in the fall. Why then do the women also come on these pilgrimages to the tabernacle?"

And Naomi was very angry with Elias for having come between her and Boaz just when she had fixed his thoughts upon Ruth. And she shouted up at Elias: "We are told that the Lord God of Israel made his covenant in the wilderness with all the children of Israel, the men and the women and even the little ones. And when Moses instructed the children of Israel to build the tabernacle, the sanctuary of the Lord God of Israel, *they came, both men and women, as many as were willing hearted and brought brooches and earrings and fringe rings and armlets of gold . . .* And we are told," said Naomi, "that *all the women that were wise hearted did spin with their hands and brought what they had spun, the blue and the purple, the scarlet and the fine linen. And all the women whose hearts stirred them up in wisdom spun the goat's hair . . .* And we are told," said Naomi, "that *the children of Israel brought freewill offerings unto the Lord; every man and woman, whose heart made them willing to bring for all their work which the Lord had commanded to be made by the hands of Moses.* And that," said Naomi, "is why the women go along with the men to the sanctuary of the Lord God of Israel." And with that she turned her donkey and rode away from Elias and Boaz.

And Boaz rebuked Elias for having offended the old woman in questioning the right of the women to go to the tabernacle they had helped to build.

"But," said Elias, "they make our dangerous journey to Shiloh still more difficult and dangerous. See there," and he pointed to the walls of Jerusalem which they were approaching, "see the Jebusites waiting on their walls to molest us while we pass by on the road beneath them."

And Boaz told Elias to sound an alarum on his ram's horn. And when the throng had come to a halt, Boaz ordered that all the women, the old men and the young lads move to the eastern side of the road so that the fighting men would form a guard between them and the Jebusites as they passed by the walls of Jerusalem; and he told the men to have ready to hand the weapons they carried concealed among the baskets of grain—the archers their bows and arrows and the others their clubs and spears and swords.

And left-handed Gibbor, drawing the knife from his right thigh shouted, "Let them cast but one stone upon us and we will stop and take the city from them! We have waited long enough since Joshua brought our fathers into this promised land which is not yet ours!" And young Joel piped up as he swung his sling: "Let us drive them out now!"

But Boaz silenced them saying: "You speak like witless children. If we have not yet won all this land which the Lord God of Israel promised our fathers it is because of our backsliding." And he sent young Joel back among the women and commanded the men that there be no show of arms or threat to the Jebusites except if they attacked the pilgrims. "For they are strong within their great walls," said Boaz, "and this is not a journey for conquest but for peaceful thanksgiving to the Lord." Then he went to the standard bearer and took the flag of the lion of Judah and rode ahead on Yohfe his stallion.

And so the throng went on toward Jerusalem, the women and the weak guarded by the men. And as they came near to the city they heard the sounds of celebration on the high place just within the wall—the seductive songs and the drunken shouts of the revelers and the dreadful wailing of their first-born under the sacrificial knife. . . . And the Jebusites perched on the great wall of their city did not molest the Israelites as they passed but they called down to them saying: "Why do you go up to Shiloh—to worship an unknown God?"

"Turn aside here and sacrifice with us to Baal on our high place."

"We have warm-blooded babes more precious to the gods than any lamb or ram."

"Bring your women up into the grove of Ashtar who will make them fertile."

"Come roast your fatlings on our fires and eat and drink and lie with us before Baal and Ashtar who will repay you a hundredfold for your sacrifices. . . ."

But none among the Israelites answered them as they went by. Only the shrill voice of Zvuv was heard as he rode between the men and the women exhorting them: "Remember what befell the children of Israel when Israel abode in Shittim. *And the people began to commit whoredom with the daughters of Moab; for they called the people unto the sacrifice of their gods; and the people did eat and bowed down to their gods. And Israel joined himself unto Baal-Peor: and the anger of the Lord was kindled against Israel. And the Lord said unto Moses, Take all the chiefs of the people, and hang them up before the sun, that the fierce anger of the Lord may turn away from Israel. And Moses said unto the judges of Israel, Slay ye every one his men that have joined themselves to Baal . . ."*

And no man among the Israelites raised his weapon, even Gibbor withheld his hidden sword; only young Joel could not resist raising his sling and sending a small stone clattering against the great wall of Jerusalem. And after they had ridden by the city of the Jebusites without mishap the men no longer rode to one side guarding the women but mingled with them again and the young men resumed their singing; but they did not gather again about Ruth because they remembered that she was a daughter of Moab their enemy. Ruth rode thereafter only with Naomi.

And as the Israelites rode northward beyond Jerusalem into the land of Benjamin, Zvuv, sitting backwards upon his bony beast so as to face the people as he rode, raised up his voice again and said: "Hear me now, fathers and mothers of Bethlehem who have daughters, lest you be moved to give them in marriage to the men of Benjamin. Hear now the tale which is told in our Book of Remembrance and which has to do with a journey along this very road up from Bethlehem in Judah to Gibeah in Benjamin. . . ."

Then Naomi said to Ruth: "That is a long story." And she took out her spinning whorl and wool and spun a thread as they rode.

And those within earshot heard as they rode the harsh voice of Zvuv rising and falling on the sunny breeze: *And it came to pass . . . that there was a certain Levite sojourning on the farther side of the hill country of Ephraim who took to him a concubine out of Bethlehem in Judah.*

And Ruth asked Naomi: "Who are these Levites?"

Naomi said: "They are the tribe of priests of Israel who have no single dwelling place in the land."

And Ruth listened again to Zvuv:

And his concubine played the harlot and went away from him to her father's house in Bethlehem and was there for the space of four months.

Naomi said: "Now is it likely that she would have gone to her father's house had she played the harlot?"

And Ruth said: "It is indeed strange," and she listened further to Zvuv:

And her husband arose, and went after her to speak kindly unto her, to bring her back, taking his servant with him and a couple of asses . . .

And Ruth said: "He would appear to have been a saintly man, this Levite, patient and kind."

Naomi said: "That remains to be seen."

And she brought him into her father's house . . .

And Naomi said: "A woman will surely not withhold forgiveness from a man who goes after her."

And Ruth said: "But was it not he who forgave her?"

And when the father of the woman saw him he rejoiced . . .

Ruth said: "Nothing seems to make a father happier than getting rid of a daughter."

And Naomi said: "Nothing but getting rid of two daughters, as Laban did when he tricked Jacob into taking both Leah and Rachel."

And they heard the harsh voice of Zvuv blown about by the breeze: *And he abode with him three days . . . And the man rose up to depart, he and his concubine and his servant, his father-in-law said unto him, Behold now the day groweth toward evening; I pray you tarry the night . . .*

Ruth said: "My father, also, little as he loved Mahlon,

165

an Israelite, was yet pleased or perhaps relieved when Mahlon came to take me in marriage."

And tomorrow get you early on your way . . .

And Naomi said: "I remember well how timidly poor Mahlon approached him and how eagerly his gifts were received."

But the man would not tarry that night, but he rose up and departed . . .

Naomi said: "You see now that this Levite was an impatient man, accustomed to having his way as many men are."

But Ruth said nothing more, and listened to the voice of Zvuv: *When they were by Jebus, which is Jerusalem, the day was far spent; and the servant said to his master, Come, I pray, let us turn aside into this city of the Jebusites and lodge in it. And his master said to him, We will not turn aside into the city of a stranger, that is not of the children of Israel; but we will pass over to Gibeah. . . .*

And Naomi said: "As it turned out he might better have stayed with the Jebusites."

So they passed on and went their way; and the sun went down upon them near to Gibeah in the land of Benjamin. And they turned aside there to lodge in Gibeah; and he sat down in the street of the city; for there was no man took them into his house to lodge. And, behold, there came an old man from his work, out of the field at evening. And this man was of the hill country of Ephraim and he sojourned in Gibeah . . .

Naomi said: "Since this is a good old man he cannot of course have been of the tribe of Benjamin, which is in ill repute to this day."

. . . and the old man said, Whither goest thou? and whence comest thou? And the wayfarer said to him, We are passing from Bethlehem in Judah to the farther side

166

of the hill country of Ephraim, from thence am I. . . .
And the old man said, Peace be unto thee; let all thy
wants lie upon me; lodge not in the street. So he brought
him into his house, and gave the asses fodder; and they
washed their feet and did eat and drink. As they were mak-
ing their hearts merry, behold, the men of the city, certain
sons of Belial, beset the house round about, beating at
the door; and they spake to the master of the house, the
old man, saying, Bring forth the man that came into thine
house, that we may know him carnally. And the master
of the house went out to them and said to them, nay, my
brethren, I pray you, do not so wickedly, this man is come
into my house, do not this folly. Behold, here is my daugh-
ter, a maiden, and his concubine, them will I bring out . . .

Naomi said: "See now how generous with their women
kindly old men can be, and even a saintly Levite."

And Ruth said: "It would not appear from this tale
that the men of Israel are indeed any better than the men
of Moab—as thou wast wont to tell me, Naomi."

. . . So the man laid hold on his concubine and brought
her forth to them; and they knew her and abused her all
the night until the morning; and when the day began to
spring they let her go. Then came the woman in the dawn-
ing of the day, and fell down at the door of the house . . .

Naomi looked up from her spinning and saw that the
dark eyes of Ruth were filled with dismay, and Naomi
said gently: "You should know, my daughter, that even
in Israel there have been and there are yet men unto
whom the spirit of the Lord God of Israel has not entered.
And in the hearts of some the spirit of the Lord still
wrestles with the spirit of Belial."

. . . till it was light. And her husband rose up in the
morning and opened the door . . .

167

"Having left her all night in the hands of those beastly men," Naomi added bitterly.

. . . and behold, the woman, his concubine, was fallen down at the door of the house with her hands upon the threshold. And he said to her, Up and let us be going; but none answered. Then he took her up . . .

And Naomi said: "The best that can be said for him is that he did not abandon her when she had died."

. . . and the man went up unto his place. And when he was come to his house he took a knife and laid hold on his concubine and divided her, limb by limb, into twelve pieces, and sent her throughout all the borders of Israel . . .

Naomi said: "Having patiently waited all the night while the evil was done her, now he was impatient to avenge her. It is a pity that men are not as eager to avert harm as to avenge it."

Then all the children of Israel went out, and the congregation was assembled as one man, from Dan even to Beersheba, with the land of Gilead, unto the Lord at Mizpah. . . .

And Naomi said: "Now is it not strange that brothers who will not unite for peace can become as one man for war?"

. . . four hundred thousand footmen that drew sword . . .

Ruth said: "And that against their own brothers!"

And Naomi said: "And is it not strange that this mighty army has assembled but once to fight their common enemy, and that was when Deborah a woman called them. The Lord God of Israel has called his people *a peculiar treasure*. And though it is sometimes difficult to see what he treasures in them they are indeed peculiar."

And the children of Israel said, Tell us, how was this

wickedness brought to pass. And the Levite, the husband
of the woman that was murdered answered and said, I
came into Gibeah in the land of Benjamin, I and my con-
cubine, to lodge. And the men of Gibeah rose against
me . . .

And Naomi said: "Observe now the spirit of man: he
takes up arms first and then asks the cause."

. . . and my concubine they forced and she is dead.
And I took my concubine and cut her in pieces and sent
her throughout all the country of the inheritance of Israel,
for they have committed lewdness and folly in Israel. . . .

And Ruth said: "And yet, this horror of lewdness in
Israel, which I first saw in Mahlon and never in the men
of Moab, is indeed a peculiar treasure which women
should prize."

And all the people rose as one man saying . . .

And Ruth said: "But it is a pity that these men need
be as fierce in their righteousness as those in their lewdness."

Now this is the thing which we will do to Gibeah, we
will go up against it by lot; and we will take ten men of
an hundred throughout all the tribes of Israel, and an
hundred of a thousand, and a thousand out of ten thou-
sand . . .

And Ruth said: "And is it not wonderful that with no
king to command them and to force them to do this, yet
the men of Israel could rise up as one man and say what
they all willed to do!"

Naomi said: "The children of Israel are indeed fearful
and wonderful."

So all the men of Israel were gathered against the city,
knit together, as one man. And the tribes of Israel sent
men through all the tribe of Benjamin, saying, What

*wickedness is this that is come to pass among you? Now
therefore deliver up the men, the sons of Belial, which
are in Gibeah, that we may put them to death, and put
away evil from Israel. But Benjamin would not hearken
to the voice of their brethren the children of Israel. And
the children of Benjamin gathered themselves together out
of the cities unto Gibeah, to go out to battle against the
children of Israel.*

And Ruth said to Naomi: "But were they not all the
children of Israel? It is a dreadful thing that brothers
should turn upon each other in hatred."

Naomi said: "Though they were all the sons of one
father, they were not of one mother: Benjamin, like Joseph, was born of beloved Rachel, while the others were
the sons of Leah and Bilhah and Zilpah whom Jacob the
father of all Israel did not love as he had loved Rachel.
And as the brothers of Joseph turned upon him and sold
him into slavery in Egypt so have the sons of the brothers
of Benjamin turned upon his sons. Even the sons of one
mother often do not love one another. My Mahlon and
Chilion though they had one mother and father were too
unlike to love one another. Chilion despised and envied
Mahlon for his frailty and my tenderness which it won
him; and Mahlon envied and despised Chilion for his
strength and lustfulness."

And Ruth looked upon Boaz bearing the flag of the
lion of Judah, and riding ahead of the throng on Yohfe
with Elias on his right hand and Gibbor on his left, and
Ruth said: "Had I two sons I would strive to make them
both to be like unto their father and then they would be
like unto each other and would love one another." And
envisioning what she had said Ruth ceased listening a
while to the voice of Zvuv:

And the children of Benjamin were numbered on that day out of the cities twenty and six thousand men that drew sword, besides the inhabitants of Gibeah, which were numbered seven hundred chosen men lefthanded; every one could sling stones at an hairbreadth, and not miss . . .

And young Joel, who had left his aunt Reba and his grandfather Tobias to ride behind Boaz, raised his small voice and cried: "And I too can sling a stone at a hairbreadth," and when Boaz turned to look upon him he showed Boaz his sling.

And Boaz asked where had he got it, and the boy told him how Ruth the Moabitess had made it for him and had taught him to use it; and Joel said: "For she wished that she had a son just like me whom she might teach to fight the enemies of Israel when they come to molest us."

Boaz said: "Did she indeed?" And he looked to where Ruth was riding nearby with Naomi.

And Joel said to Boaz: "I wish that I had been among those who fought the Benjamites!"

And Boaz said gently: "Had I a son just like you, Joel, I would teach him not to wish for war with his brothers."

Nevertheless the lad listened eagerly to the tale Zvuv was telling:

And the children of Israel arose and went up to Bethel and asked counsel of God; and they said, Who shall go up for us first to battle against the children of Benjamin? And the Lord said, Judah shall go up first. And the children of Israel rose up in the morning and encamped against Gibeah. And the men of Israel went out to battle against Benjamin . . .

Then Joel said boastfully: "Being a son of Judah I should have been one of the first to go against Benjamin."

And Gibbor the Benjamite who sat upon the burdened camel beside Boaz, listening unhappily to the story, scowled at the lad.

And the children of Benjamin came forth out of Gibeah and destroyed down to the ground on that day twenty and two thousand men of Israel. . . .

And Gibbor turned to the boy saying: "Now do you wish you were there?" And Joel, chagrined, did not answer him.

And the children of Israel went up and wept before the Lord until evening; and they asked of the Lord, saying, Shall I draw nigh to battle against the children of Benjamin, my brethren? And the Lord said go up against him. And the children of Israel came near against the children of Benjamin the second day. And Benjamin went forth against them out of Gibeah the second day, and destroyed down to the ground again eighteen thousand men of Israel . . .

Then Gibbor turned again to the unhappy boy saying: "Now do you wish you were there? Even the Lord did not help them."

And Boaz rebuked Gibbor saying: "Do not plague the lad. Had I a son like him I would wish he need never know such warfare; but who knows when Israel shall live in lasting peace, though we pray for peace and greet each other with 'Peace.' " And to Joel he said: "Listen now to Zvuv and see what will happen. You will learn that the Lord does what is right, but in his own time."

Then all the children of Israel, and all the people, went up and came to Bethel and wept and sat there before the Lord, for the ark of the covenant of God was there in those days, and Phineas, the son of Eleazar, the son of Aaron, stood before it in those days. And the children of

*Israel asked of the Lord, saying, Shall I yet again go out
to battle against the children of Benjamin my brother,
or shall I cease? And the Lord said, Go up; for tomorrow
I shall deliver him into your hand. And Israel set liers in
wait round about Gibeah.*

And Naomi said to Ruth: "Now you shall hear of the
trick my wise Elimelech devised to overcome the Benjamites."

And Ruth said: "But if the Lord God of Israel had
promised them victory why need they have devised a trick
to accomplish it?"

Naomi said: "That is a question I cannot answer. All I
can tell you is that the Lord makes nothing easy for man,
even for his chosen people. Though he parted the Red
Sea for them, he first hardened the heart of Pharaoh ten
times to prevent their departure from Egypt. In six days
the Lord created the earth and all that is in it; but he
makes us bear a child nine months and then suffer to
bring it from the womb."

And Ruth, looking to where Boaz spoke with the boy
Joel riding beside him, said: "Indeed the Lord does not
make it easy for us women to bring to pass what we want."
And she sighed as she listened again to Zvuv:

*And the children of Israel went up against the children
of Benjamin on the third day, and set themselves in array
against Gibeah as at the other times. And the children of
Benjamin went out against them and were drawn away
from the city; and they began to smite and kill . . .*

And Joel said anxiously: "Did not the Lord come to
their help?"

*But the children of Israel said, Let us flee and draw
them away from the city into the highways. . . .*

And Boaz said to Joel: "Listen my lad, and you will

173

learn. But pray God that you never need use this knowledge."

. . . because they trusted unto the liers in wait which they had set against Gibeah. And the liers in wait hastened and rushed upon Gibeah . . .

And Joel exulted: "That was clever of them was it not, Boaz? If I were there I would be first among the liers in wait."

. . . and smote all the city at the edge of the sword. Now the appointed sign between the men of Israel and the liers in wait was that they should make a great cloud of smoke rise up out of the city. And the men of Israel turned in the battle . . .

And Gibbor said sourly: "It was only through guile, not by their strength that they won."

. . . and the Benjamites looked behind them and, behold, the whole of the city went up in a pillar of smoke to heaven. And they turned their backs before the men of Israel and fled unto the way of the wilderness; but the battle followed hard after them . . .

And Joel cried to Gibbor: "Then why did you not turn upon us if you were so strong!"

. . . and the Lord smote Benjamin before Israel; and the children of Israel destroyed of Benjamin that day twenty and five thousand . . .

Gibbor said contemptuously: "They could not have done it but for the help of the Lord."

. . . the entire city and the cattle and all that they found . . .

And again young Joel said enviously: "I wish that I had been there!"

. . . and the men of Israel swore at Mizpah saying, There shall not any of us give his daughter unto Benjamin to wife. . . .

174

"And all for the sake of a single woman!" grumbled Gibbor as Zvuv ended the story.

Nevertheless when the men and women of Judah came to the gates of Gibeah in Benjamin, which was the home of Gibbor, many Benjamites, headed by their standard bearing the wolf of Benjamin, came out to join the pilgrims from Judah. They were mostly men, there being a great lack of women among the Benjamites, and the young men among them, strong and lusty like Gibbor, sought to ride with the maidens of Judah. But the fathers of the maidens rode close behind their daughters and dissuaded the ardent young men, reminding them of the oath their fathers had taken. But when some young Benjamites, drawn by the beauty of Ruth, clustered about her singing her praises Naomi did not dissuade them because she saw from afar the fire of jealousy they kindled in the grave gray eyes of Boaz.

And so the pilgrims rode northward out of Benjamin up into the hill country of Ephraim, Joseph's younger son— he whom old Jacob, dying in Egypt, had placed before Manasseh his elder brother when he blessed them both. And the land of Ephraim was a beautiful land with streams gushing forth from the rocks, watering the gardens and vineyards on the hillsides, and with forests of oak and yew on the uplands whence through the clear sunny air the pilgrims could see the snowy heads of Mount Hermon and Lebanon high in the sky like white clouds far to the north.

So they went past Ramah and Ai to Bethel where they all halted to rest and to feed their beasts in a field in which stood a pillar of stone. And there was an ancient oak and under it an old tomb which was said to be Deborah's grave. And eastward on a mountain they could see the altar which Abraham set up when he first came

175

into Canaan. And there in the field they were joined by Ephraimite pilgrims headed by their standard bearing the fruitful bough of Joseph their father.

And some of the Benjamites, uncouth young men like Gibbor, soiled the field wherein the pilgrims were resting, by leaving their excrement exposed upon it; and Zvuv fell upon these men, angrily berating them for their uncleanness, reminding them how Moses had ordered the children of Israel in the desert to carry about them paddles of wood with which to cover their excrement, saying: *For the Lord thy God walketh in the midst of thy camp.*

Then Zvuv, mounting upon a hillock by the pillar of stone that stood in the field, told how Jacob the father of all Israel had once stopped there in that very place to rest: *And Jacob went out from Beer-sheba and went toward Haran. And he lighted upon a certain place, and tarried there all night, because the sun was set; and he took one of the stones of the place, and put it under his head, and lay down in that place to sleep. And he dreamed, and behold a ladder set up on the earth and the top of it reached to heaven. And behold the angels of God ascending and descending on it.*

Then Ruth said to Naomi: "You would think that what the Lord God had done at the tower of Babel would have stopped men from trying even in dreams to reach up into heaven."

And Naomi said: "There is no stopping those dreamers."

Zvuv said: *And behold the Lord stood above it and said, I am the Lord, the God of Abraham, thy father, and the God of Isaac: the land whereon thou liest, to thee will I give it, and to thy seed; and thy seed shall be as the dust of the earth, and thou shalt spread abroad to the west, and to the east, and to the north, and to the south; and in thee*

176

and in thy seed shall all the families of the earth be blest. And, behold, I am with thee, and will keep thee wherever thou goest, and will bring thee again into this land; for I will not leave thee, until I have done that which I have spoken to thee of.

And Elias said to Boaz: "It is long since that promise was made us, yet we are still but a handful here in the midst of many enemies who do not look upon us and our God as a blessing; and we go up to the Lord our God bearing arms lest the other families of the earth destroy us on the way."

And Zvuv said: *And Jacob awaked out of his sleep, and he said, Surely the Lord is in this place; and I knew it not. And he was afraid, and said, How fearful is this place! This is none other than the house of God, and this is the gate of heaven. And Jacob rose up early in the morning and took the stone that he had put under his head and set it up for a pillar, and poured oil upon the top of it. And he called the name of that place Bethel. . . .*

And Gibbor said to Boaz: "Our father Jacob must have been a lusty fellow seeing that he went and got himself four wives in Haran and begot twelve sons and a daughter after setting up here a dripping pillar to God as do the peoples of Canaan to this day, which we the children of Israel are now forbidden to do. And he must have been a shrewd fellow, for did he not here make a bargain with God, offering a tithe if the Lord brought him back to his father's house?"

Boaz said: "That was long, long ago before Moses brought us up out of Egypt and brought down for us from Mount Sinai the laws and commandments of the Almighty."

"And now," said Zvuv, "the house of the Lord God of

177

Israel is at Shiloh as our father Jacob foretold it would be in his blessing of Judah. And this day do we go up to Shiloh with our offerings to the Lord, not as do other peoples to bribe their greedy gods, but to give thanks to the one God whose will is unchanging and whose laws we come there to learn and to heed. And he that turns away his ear from hearing the law, even his prayer is an abomination to the Lord who wants no bribe from his people Israel. Nor does the Lord lust like the gods of other peoples for the blood of his children and the lewdness of his sons and daughters. In witness whereof he sent to our father Abraham a scapegoat to sacrifice for his son, Isaac, and he destroyed Sodom and Gomorrah for their lewdness. And though we go now to offer the first of our harvests to the Lord, and though it is the duty of the men of Israel in this harvest season to increase the fruitfulness of the women of Israel in marriage, do not let such lustful thoughts entice you to the abominations of the Jebusites, the Ammonites, and the Moabites. Far different from the rites of spring on the heathen high places is our celebration of this the Feast of Weeks at Shiloh. . . ."

And indeed it was different from the spring rites in Moab, as Ruth saw when they arrived in Shiloh at nightfall and joined the multitude which had come from the tribes to the north and from eastward across Jordan. For the women were separated from the men and encamped apart from them for the night on a hillside above the place before the court of the tabernacle where the host of men were encamped around the standards of their tribes, around the lion of Judah, the wolf of Benjamin, the fruitful bough of Ephraim and Manasseh the two sons of Joseph, the strong crouching ass of Issachar, the ship of Zebulon, the hind of Naphthali from beside the blue Sea of Kinnereth, and the serpent of Dan from far to the north by snowy Mount Hermon. And the men of Israel did not carouse in the night but busied themselves bringing their offerings of beasts and of grain to the entrance of the fore-court of the tabernacle which was dark now but for the light of the eternal lamp within it and the smouldering fire upon the altar before it in readiness for the sacrifices on the morrow.

And as Ruth and Naomi lay down to rest among the women on the hill Ruth said: "It seems strange that the men of Israel set their women apart from them when they assemble before their God. It would seem from this that they think not more but less of their women than do the men of Moab—that they consider us creatures unworthy of the attention of the Lord."

Naomi said: "It may seem so, my daughter; but it is because they well know the power of women to rouse their passions that they place us apart from them before the Lord; it is because they fear that with us amongst them they may be moved to turn to the abominations of the high places. It is not women they think the less of but their own lustfulness. Sleep now, my daughter, and you will see in the morning how different are these men of Israel before their God from the men before the gods of Moab."

And indeed Ruth saw that it was so when she was awakened at dawn by the shrill sweet blasts of silver trumpets and she rose up and went to stand with Naomi among the garlanded women gathered upon the flowery hillside singing together as the sun slowly rose:

Make a joyful noise unto the Lord,
  all ye lands,
Serve the Lord with gladness:
Come before his presence singing.

And from the camp below, the risen men still in twilight sang:

Know ye the Lord he is God:
It is he that made us, we are his;
We are his people, the sheep of his pasture.

Then from the risen sun shafts of light fell upon the tabernacle within its many-pillared court, curtained in blue and purple and scarlet. And the tabernacle of acacia beams set in sockets of silver, with curtains of fine twined linen blue and purple and scarlet and ram's skins dyed red, gleamed like a great jewel box bearing its treasure of holiness; for it held the ark of the covenant within a veil of blue and purple and scarlet lighted by the tall candelabrum of pure beaten gold with six flowering branches, bearing the seven cups of pure olive oil. Between the tabernacle and the smoldering altar of sacrifice in the forecourt stood a long table of acacia overlain with pure gold with a rim of wrought gold like a crown within which were ranged the rows of fine shewbread brought by the women of all the tribes of Israel. And it pleased Ruth to know that her loaves were there among them.

And there came into the court four young priests, Levites in breeches of blue and coats of purple and girdles of scarlet, and they went to a laver of brass and washed their hands and their feet, and they lit the incense upon the incense altar of acacia overlain with gold which stood before the tabernacle and then went about the court sprinkling perfume of spices everywhere. From the incense altar rose up a cloud fragrant with pure frankincense, and from the sprinkled perfume came the odors of sweet spices —of myrrh and cinnamon, calamus and cassia. And the priests went to stand by the great altar of sacrifice, built foursquare of acacia with four horns of brass at its corners, with its firepans and gratings of gleaming brass as well as its pots and shovels, its basins and fleshhooks. Then the men of Israel came into the forecourt, each bearing his basket of first fruits, the poor men their plain wicker baskets, the rich ones their intricate ones overlain with wrought silver, but singing together with all their might:

> Enter his gates with thanksgiving,
> Into his courts with praise:
> Give thanks unto him and bless his name.

And from the hillside above came the sweet voices of the women:

> For the Lord is good;
> His mercy endureth forever;
> And his faithfulness unto all generations.

Each Israelite as he handed his basket to one of the priests said aloud: I profess this day unto the Lord thy God that I am come into the land which the Lord swore unto our fathers to give us.

And the priests took the baskets and set them down before the altar and took from each basket a handful of the grain to put upon the altar together with oil and frankincense for a burnt offering which made a high heap burning higher and higher.

And when the men were all gathered before the altar they lifted up their voices and said as with one voice: Ready to perish was my father. And he went down into

Egypt and sojourned there, few in number; and he be-
came there a nation, great, mighty and populous: and the
Egyptians evilly treated us, and afflicted us, and laid upon
us hard bondage: and we cried unto the Lord, the God
of our fathers, and the Lord heard our voice, and saw our
affliction, and our toil and our oppression: and the Lord
brought us forth out of Egypt with a mighty hand, and
with an outstretched arm, and with great and terrible
signs, and with wonders: and he brought us into this place,
and hath given us this land, a land flowing with milk and
honey. And now, behold, I have brought the first of the
fruit of the ground, which thou, O Lord, hast given me.

The priests fed more fire to the high heap of offerings
upon the altar, and they waved sheaves of the first fruits—
the wave offerings—before the fiery altar.

And as the many voices rose up in a ringing shout to the
brightening heavens Ruth watched the great flames rise
up from the altar where these Israelites, instead of sacri-
ficing the first-born fruit of their loins under a bloody
knife, sacrificed in cleansing fire the first fruit of their
fields to the Creator of the Universe who in his bountiful
mercy had given them more than their needs.

Then the Levites stood before the fire and spoke unto
the men of Israel with a loud voice saying: *Cursed be the*
man that maketh a graven or molten image, an abomina-
tion unto the Lord, the work of the hands of the crafts-
man, and setteth it up in secret.

And the men answered them with a loud shout:
"Amen!" that was echoed by the voices of the women upon
the hill.

And the Levites said: *Cursed be he that setteth lightly*
his father and his mother.

And the men below and the women above answered
them: "Amen!"

182

And thus the Levites pronounced curse after curse and the people answered them:

Cursed be he that maketh the blind to wander out of the way.

"Amen!"

Cursed be he that wresteth the judgment of the stranger, fatherless, and widow.

"Amen!"

Cursed be he that lieth with his father's wife; because he hath uncovered his father's skirt.

"Amen!"

Cursed be he that lieth with any manner of beast.

"Amen!"

Cursed be he that lieth with his sister, the daughter of his father, or the daughter of his mother.

"Amen!"

Cursed be he that lieth with his mother in law.

"Amen!"

Cursed be he that smiteth his neighbor in secret.

"Amen!"

Cursed be he that taketh reward to slay an innocent person.

"Amen!"

Cursed be he that confirmeth not the words of this law to do them.

"Amen!"

Then the Levites lifted up their voices and said in unison:

And it shall come to pass, if thou shalt hearken diligently unto the voice of the Lord thy God, to observe to do all his commandments which I command thee this day, that the Lord thy God will set thee on high above all the nations of the earth: and all these blessings shall come upon thee, and overtake thee, if thou shalt hearken unto the voice of the Lord thy God. Blessed shalt thou be in the city, and blessed shalt thou be in the field. Blessed shall be the fruit of thy body, and the fruit of thy ground, and the fruit of thy cattle, the increase of thy kine, and the young of thy flock. Blessed shall be thy basket and thy kneading trough. Blessed shalt thou be when thou comest in, and blessed shalt thou be when thou goest out. The Lord shall cause thine enemies that rise up against thee to be smitten before thee: they shall come out against thee one way, and shall flee before thee seven ways. The Lord shall command the blessing upon thee in thy barns, and in all that thou puttest thine hand unto and he shall bless thee in the land which the Lord thy God giveth thee. The Lord shall establish thee for an holy people unto himself, as he hath sworn unto thee; if thou shalt keep the commandments of the Lord thy God, and walk in his ways . . .

And Ruth among the women looking down upon the men saw the tall form of Boaz among them and resolved to learn diligently the commandments of the Lord God of Israel and prayed that she might become the blessed bearer of the fruit of the body of Boaz.

. . . but it shall come to pass, if thou wilt not hearken unto the voice of the Lord thy God, to observe to do all his commandments and his statutes which I command thee this day; that all these curses shall come upon thee, and overtake thee. Cursed shalt thou be in the city, and cursed shalt thou be in the field. Cursed shall be thy basket and thy kneading trough. Cursed shall be the fruit of thy body, and the fruit of thy ground, the increase of thy kine, and the young of thy flock. Cursed shalt thou be when thou comest in, and cursed shalt thou be when thou goest out. . . . The Lord shall make the pestilence cleave unto thee, until he have consumed thee from off the land, whither thou goest in to possess it. The Lord shall smite

thee with consumption, and with fever, and with inflam-
mation, and with fiery heat, and with the sword, and with
blasting, and with mildew; and they shall pursue thee
until thou perish. And thy heaven that is over thy head
shall be brass, and the earth that is under thee shall be
iron. The Lord shall make the rain of thy land powder
and dust: from heaven shall it come down upon thee,
until thou be destroyed. The Lord shall cause thee to be
smitten before thine enemies: thou shalt go out one way
against them, and shalt flee seven ways before them: and
thou shalt be tossed to and fro among all the kingdoms of
the earth.

Then the men of Israel bowed them down and cried out:
I have not transgressed any of thy commandments, neither
have I forgotten them. I have hearkened to the voice of
the Lord my God, I have done according to all that thou
hast commanded me. Look down from thy holy habitation,
from heaven, and bless thy people Israel, and the ground
which thou hast given us, as thou swarest unto our fathers,
a land flowing with milk and honey.

Then the men rose up and brought the firstlings of
their flocks, the bullocks with gilded horns wreathed in
olive branches and the lambs for peace offerings and the
rams for sin offerings. And the priests took sharp knives
and slaughtered the animals and poured out their red
blood upon the flaming altar saying: *And whatsoever man*
there be of the house of Israel, or of the strangers that
sojourn among them, that eateth any manner of blood;
I will set my face against that soul that eateth blood, and
will cut him off from among his people. For the life of
the flesh is in the blood: and I have given it to you upon
the altar to make atonement for your souls: for it is the
blood that maketh atonement by reason of the life. There-

fore I said unto the children of Israel, No soul of you shall eat blood, neither shall any stranger that sojourneth among you eat blood. And the flesh the priests put into great pans and cauldrons to seethe over the fires the men had made for the feast; and the smell of the seething flesh rose up with the smoke and the flames.

Then drummers and flute players came and made music. And, led by Boaz the tallest among them, the young men of Israel began to dance before the mounting altar fire and the incense cloud, a circling dance in which they marched and halted by turns as they chanted of the exodus from Egypt: *And on the day that the tabernacle was reared up the cloud covered the tabernacle, even the tent of the testimony: and at even it was upon the tabernacle as it were the appearance of fire, until morning. So it was always: the cloud covered it, and the appearance of fire by night. And whenever the cloud was taken up from over the tent, then after that the children of Israel encamped. At the commandment of the Lord the children of Israel journeyed, and at the commandment of the Lord they encamped: as long as the cloud abode upon the tabernacle they remained encamped. . . .*

And the procession of dancers led by Boaz wound about the blazing altar and in and out of the incense cloud, marching and halting as they chanted of the journey and the encampment of the children of Israel; and when they marched they danced to the stirring music of the drums; and when they halted they danced to the peaceful music of the flutes: *And sometimes the cloud was a few days upon the tabernacle; then according to the commandment of the Lord they remained encamped, and according to the commandment of the Lord they journeyed. . . . Whether it were two days, or a month, or a year, that the cloud*

*tarried upon the tabernacle, abiding thereon, the children
of Israel remained encamped, and journeyed not: but
when it was taken up, they journeyed. At the commandment of the Lord they encamped, and at the commandment of the Lord they journeyed. . . .*

Then Boaz stood still in the midst of the circling dancers
and raised up his strong hands and sang aloud:

> *Give ear, ye heavens, and I will speak;*
>   *And let the earth hear the words of my mouth:*
> *My doctrine shall drop as the rain,*
>   *My speech shall distil as the dew;*
> *As the small rain upon the tender grass,*
>   *And as the showers upon the herb:*
> *For I will proclaim the name of the Lord:*
>   *Ascribe ye greatness unto our God! . . .*

And the heart of Ruth as she heard him was lifted up
and filled with longing and a great eagerness as she heard
the women about her whispering, "He is a prince among
men!"

And all the young men below raised their voices and
sang with the voice of Boaz as they danced, and he led
them again singing and dancing before the blazing altar
in a dance so full of the graceful strength of the potent
and fervent male that the women upon the hillside could
not refrain from dancing, also. And Ruth joining hands
with them danced with delight as they circled and whirled
about, tossing their garlands of flowers into the sunny
air . . . until, to the blowing of the silver trumpets, the
four young priests went into the tabernacle and parted
the purple veil of the holy of holies and took up the ark
and brought it out from within the sanctuary.

Then all music and dancing ceased; the men below

and the women above stood still as the four Levites came bearing on two long staves thrust through its four golden rings the golden ark of the covenant covered by the golden mercy seat with its two golden cherubim kneeling and spreading their great golden wings toward each other.

And following after the ark came the High Priest out of the tabernacle, a tall old man with silvery hair and beard who moved very slowly because of the weight of the gold and the jewels he wore. The miter upon his brow bore a golden plate graven with the words *Holy unto the Lord*. Two great stones of onyx set in gold upon his shoulders were carved with the names of the twelve children of Israel—six names upon each stone—and the breastplate he wore was set with twelve glowing stones: an emerald, a sapphire, a diamond, a topaz. . . . And cords of gold tied and girdled his checkered coat and his blue robe was sewn with golden bells so that there was a golden sound as he came from the tabernacle to stand before the great altar.

All the people, the men below and the women above, waited in silence and watched as the young priests bearing the golden ark circled the altar and set down their sacred burden before the silver-haired High Priest. And clouds of smoke from the altar of incense and the altar of sacrifice enveloped the golden ark and the golden winged cherubim and the bejeweled High Priest that glowed and gleamed through the fragrant mist. And the silvery voice of the High Priest rose from the mist saying: *Thus said Moses to the children of Israel: Set your heart unto all the words which I testify unto you this day; which ye shall command your children to observe, to do all the words of this law. For it is no vain thing for you; because it is your life, and through this thing you shall prolong your days upon the land, whither we go over Jordan to possess it.*

And then the four Levites raised up the mercy seat with its cherubim from off the ark, uncovering the tablets of the testimony within. And all the people, the men below and the women above, saw dimly through the mist the two graven tablets Moses brought down from Sinai after he had broken the first stones in his anger at sight of the golden calf. And the High Priest raised up his silvery voice again and spoke their ten commandments; and all the people, the men below and the women above, spoke after him, and their voices rolled up from the hill, prolonged, in a mighty echo:

Thou shalt have . . .
THOU SHALT HAVE NONE OTHER GODS BEFORE ME.
Thou shalt not make . . .
THOU SHALT NOT MAKE UNTO THEE A GRAVEN IMAGE, NOR THE LIKENESS OF ANY FORM THAT IS IN HEAVEN ABOVE, OR THAT IS IN THE EARTH BENEATH, OR THAT IS IN THE WATER UNDER THE EARTH: THOU SHALT NOT BOW DOWN THYSELF UNTO THEM, NOR SERVE THEM: FOR I THE LORD THY GOD AM A JEALOUS GOD, VISITING THE INIQUITY OF THE FATHERS UPON THE CHILDREN, UPON THE THIRD AND UPON THE FOURTH GENERATION OF THEM THAT HATE ME; AND SHEWING MERCY UNTO THOUSANDS, OF THEM THAT LOVE ME AND KEEP MY COMMANDMENTS.
Thou shalt not take . . .
THOU SHALT NOT TAKE THE NAME OF THE LORD THY GOD IN VAIN; FOR THE LORD WILL NOT HOLD HIM GUILTLESS THAT TAKETH HIS NAME IN VAIN.
Remember the Sabbath . . .
REMEMBER THE SABBATH DAY, TO KEEP IT HOLY. SIX

DAYS SHALT THOU LABOR, AND DO ALL THY WORK: BUT THE SEVENTH DAY IS A SABBATH UNTO THE LORD THY GOD: IN IT THOU SHALT NOT DO ANY WORK, THOU, NOR THY SON, NOR THY DAUGHTER, THY MANSERVANT, NOR THY MAID- SERVANT, NOR THY CATTLE, NOR THY STRANGER THAT IS WITHIN THY GATES: FOR IN SIX DAYS THE LORD MADE HEAVEN AND EARTH, THE SEA, AND ALL THAT IN THEM IS, AND RESTED THE SEVENTH DAY: WHEREFORE THE LORD BLESSED THE SABBATH DAY, AND HALLOWED IT.

Honour thy father . . .

HONOUR THY FATHER AND THY MOTHER: THAT THY DAYS MAY BE LONG UPON THE LAND WHICH THE LORD THY GOD GIVETH THEE.

Thou shalt not . . .

THOU SHALT NOT MURDER.

Thou shalt not . . .

THOU SHALT NOT COMMIT ADULTERY.

Thou shalt not . . .

THOU SHALT NOT STEAL.

Thou shalt not bear . . .

THOU SHALT NOT BEAR FALSE WITNESS AGAINST THY NEIGHBOR.

Thou shalt not covet . . .

THOU SHALT NOT COVET THY NEIGHBOR'S HOUSE, THOU SHALT NOT COVET THY NEIGHBOR'S WIFE, NOR HIS MAN- SERVANT, NOR HIS MAIDSERVANT, NOR HIS OX, NOR HIS ASS, NOR ANYTHING THAT IS THY NEIGHBOR'S.

And then a great shout rose up from all the men: *Hear, O Israel, the Lord our God, the Lord is One!* and rolled up to the high heavens of the land of Israel.

And from the hill above came the answering cry of the women: *And thou shalt love the Lord, thy God, with all thy heart, with all thy soul, and with all thy might!*

Then the women ran down from the hill and met the men who came swarming from the forecourt; and those who loved and desired one another among the men and the maidens went together before the young priests and were there and then married by them and blessed with the blessing which Moses had told to Aaron:

The Lord bless thee, and keep thee:
The Lord make his face to shine upon thee, and be
gracious unto thee:
The Lord lift up his countenance upon thee, and give
thee peace.

And there was great rejoicing among the multitude, with music and song. The people sang:

God be merciful unto us, and bless us,
And cause his face to shine upon us;
That thy way may be known upon earth,
Thy saving health among all the nations.
Let all the peoples praise thee, O God,
Let all the peoples praise thee.

And Naomi looked about for Boaz, hoping to bring Ruth near to him at that auspicious time. And she saw that he was with Gibbor and the men of Benjamin in among the multitude of men and women who, after the marriages had been made, were gathered about the pans, the kettles, the cauldrons and pots in which the flesh of the sacrifices seethed and roasted. And the young priests were there crying out: "Come all and eat of the meat of sacrifice! For Moses said: *When ye sacrifice a sacrifice of thanksgiving unto the Lord on the same day shall it be eaten: Ye shall leave none of it until the morning.* Come all now and eat!"

Naomi went there with Ruth and stood within sight of

Boaz as they partook of the savory food with the others. And the servants of the priests came with their three-toothed flesh hooks and thrust them into the pots, and what the flesh hooks brought up they took away for the priests.

And Gibbor eating heartily said to Boaz: "I wish I had been born a Levite instead of a Benjamite. For it is no hard life the young priests have here, living off the fat of the land which we bring them. And some say that the sons of the High Priest lie freely with the maidens of Shiloh who come to do service at the tabernacle. Nor can I blame them for that, seeing that the maidens are plentiful in Shiloh, and pretty and merry too. But it seems unjust to us, the men of Benjamin, that because of something our fathers did we should be denied the right to marry the women of any other tribe than our own. You are a judge, Boaz, do you not think it unjust?"

But Boaz did not answer him. Boaz was looking away to where Ruth, sitting among the pretty maidens of Shiloh, outshone them all, like the moon among many stars.

Then another of the sons of Benjamin also spoke of their need, and of the injustice done them, saying: "We, the sons of Benjamin, ask why should this come to pass in Israel, that there should be one tribe lacking, that Benjamin should be blotted out. For though we were given the four hundred virgins who were saved alive from the destruction of Jabesh-Gilead, those have not sufficed us; and what shall we do now for wives for those who still remain unwed, since so many women were destroyed in Benjamin during that dreadful war which our fathers fought over a wayward concubine?"

Then Boaz said to the Benjamite: "It is no use your

asking if it is unjust. You have heard how the men of Israel swore, saying: *Cursed be he that gives a wife to Benjamin.* And it is no use your asking the fathers of Israel to give you their daughters. If you must have wives you will have to go to the women you wish and take them for yourselves." And he looked again upon the cluster of maidens among whom Ruth was sitting, eating and laughing with them, for she had found favor among the many maidens of Shiloh who remained unmarried because there were more of them than there were young men in Ephraim to seek them in marriage.

And Gibbor cried: "I'll be a son of Belial, if you have not given us the answer, Boaz!" And he turned to the men of Benjamin saying: "Let us seek out, each one of us, a maiden of Shiloh to his liking, and take her and carry her off to Benjamin at the end of today's assembly."

Then Boaz said to him: "If I were one of the sons of Benjamin I would not do it today, for there are too many of their fathers, the men of Shiloh, about; and they will surely prevent you. Nor would it be proper to do so here before the tabernacle which is for the service of the Lord. But I would wait until the wine harvest, when the maidens of Shiloh come out to dance in their vineyards; then would I lie in wait with my brothers, and every man would get himself the wife he had chosen and carry her off. And thus their fathers, the men of Shiloh, would not have broken the oath; and you would have got the women you need to build up your cities again."

And Gibbor said: "You are indeed a wise man, and worthy to judge in Israel, Boaz. And do you say that we may do so?"

Boaz said thoughtfully: "I know of no law against it, Gibbor, and it is surely the Lord's wish that every man should have his woman—did he not give Eve to Adam for a helpmeet for him?" Then Boaz, still looking upon Ruth among the maidens of Shiloh, bethought himself further and said: "I have said what I would do were I a son of Benjamin. But as a man of Judah I am myself bound by the oath of my fathers. Now this is a matter too difficult for me to decide. And Moses said: *If there arise a matter too hard for thee in judgment thou shalt come unto the priests.* So shall I take this matter to the High Priest. Do you, Gibbor, come with me to the High Priest, and then you shall tell your brethren of Benjamin what is his judgment."

And they did so. Boaz went with Gibbor to where the High Priest stood between the smoking altars in the forecourt of the tabernacle, gleaming in his bejeweled vestments like a silvery cloud. And Boaz stood before him saying: "I have come to ask your judgment in a matter that is too hard for me." And he told him of the need of the men of Benjamin and of the way in which they might get them wives without the consent of the fathers of the maidens of Shiloh.

The High Priest bethought himself and said: "We know that the Lord our God visits the iniquity of the fathers upon the children, unto the third and unto the fourth generation. Yet do we know also that in the beginning the Lord God said: *It is not good that the man should be alone,* and he gave Eve to Adam. So let the sons of Benjamin do what is right in their own eyes in this matter."

And Gibbor joyfully hastened away to tell the Benjamites of the judgment of the High Priest.

But Boaz remained standing before the High Priest, who said to him: "And you, Boaz, are you not seeking a wife for yourself?"

Boaz said: "I have sought among the maidens of Bethlehem; and none among the daughters of my tribe has found favor in my sight. Now there has come to sojourn in Judah a woman who has moved my heart, but she is a stranger."

And the High Priest said: "Have we not been commanded: *The stranger that sojourneth with you shall be unto you as the homeborn among you, and thou shalt love him as thyself.* Does this woman live among you like a God-fearing daughter of Israel?"

And Boaz answered: "She is the widow of Mahlon, son of Elimelech, and lives with her mother-in-law Naomi, the widow of Elimelech, to whom she has sworn saying: Thy people shall be my people and thy God my God. And she has come here today bringing an offering of shewbread."

And the High Priest said: "Whose daughter is she?"

Boaz said: "She is the daughter of Moab, our enemy."

The High Priest was gravely silent. Then he said: "Moses himself took to wife Zipporah, the daughter of Jethro, a priest of the Midianites who are strangers to Israel and our enemies. And in the matter of marriage every man does what is right in his own eyes, and no man can properly advise another nor pass judgment upon him. For marriage, my son, is in any event a risk: a man may find himself married to a wayward harlot or a cold contentious creature, or to a woman who is, as the Lord God intended when he gave Eve to Adam for a helpmeet, a joy and a comfort to him by day and by night. And this risk the man takes whether the woman he marries be a stranger or a daughter of his own people. True it is that the risk seems greater when the woman comes to him from afar, but do you not know men in your own city who are unhappily married to women who have never set foot outside the walls?"

Boaz said: "Indeed I do." And from where they stood he could hear the harsh voice of Zvuv haranguing the newly married couples as they came from the priests—speaking to them of their duty to be fruitful and multiply not for their own gratification but for the greater glory of the Lord God of Israel. And Boaz said: "Indeed it is for that reason that I have sometimes been loath to choose for a wife a maiden from among the daughters of Bethlehem lest it be as unhappy a choice as many among their mothers—foolish and frivolous or contentious women—that I have there witnessed."

Then the High Priest smiled and he said: "Wise or unwise, the choice remains in the heart of the man himself. Only Adam was spared that choice by the Lord God of the Universe."

Boaz said: "And that is not the only matter in which the Lord God has not given man a clear vision of the way he should choose."

And the High Priest said: "Indeed, my son, it is true that it has been given to few men to penetrate the thick darkness where God is, and draw near to him and know his will and his judgment. We the children of Israel have been fortunate in having had Moses to do so and to bring down to us the statutes and commandments of the Lord."

And Boaz said: "But even so, Moses has not made all the way clear to us. Just now, in the matter of wives for the men of Benjamin, you could find no single guidance for them. And when Ruth the woman of Moab made her shewbread and the women of Bethlehem came complaining that Moses had said: *Neither from the hand of a foreigner shall ye offer the bread of your God,* I could cite them Moses also: *If a stranger sojourn with you and will offer an offering——*"

The pale eyes of the High Priest twinkled as he said: "I know the commandment. It was clever of you, my son."

And Boaz continued: "But consider also that the stranger we take in to sojourn among us may come to serve our enemies. And though Moses commanded our fathers to destroy without mercy those enemies who rose up against us, yet did he also say: *If thou meet thine enemy's ox or his ass going astray, thou shalt surely bring it back to him again.*"

The High Priest said: "Long ago—even before the Lord God spoke to Moses—he revealed to our father Abraham that the way of the Lord is *to do justice and judgment.* To return the ox of your enemy is to do justice; to destroy the evil that is your enemy is good judgment. Unless there be judgment, the evil will destroy the good on this earth. And if you do injustice to your enemy you will learn in time to do injustice to all. To do righteousness and justice is more acceptable to the Lord than sacrifice. *Keep my commandments, says the Lord, and you shall live. Hate the evil and love the good and establish judgment in the gate, and the Lord, the God of hosts, will be gracious unto the children of Israel.* Our God is a God of love and of wisdom, hating only evil, which is not only the destroyer of the good but the creator of still more evil. And God said to Moses: *Thou shalt speak unto all that are wise-hearted, whom I have filled with the spirit of wisdom.* You are known to be a wise judge in Judah, Boaz. Let your love and your wisdom serve yourself as well as your people, and the Lord will be gracious to you as well as to them."

Yet Boaz continued pleading for counsel: "But it is not easy to be a judge in Israel! In my judging I find that it is not easy for a man to know justice from injustice, which are often as difficult to distinguish as good from evil."

Then the High Priest spoke again, and his old eyes and his withered lips half hidden in his silvery beard smiled again upon the strong troubled countenance of Boaz: "Our father Jacob had to wrestle with the angel of the Lord for his blessing. And even Moses, being himself but a man, could not make it easy for men to know good from evil, justice from injustice, which as you say are often difficult to distinguish one from the other. Consider that God said to Moses when the children of Israel were still on their way here to the promised land: *I will deliver the inhabitants of the land into your hand; and thou shalt drive them out before thee. Thou shalt make no covenant with them nor with their gods lest they make thee sin against me.* Nevertheless did he also say that the stranger who sojourns among us shall be treated as one of us. There must sometimes have been, even in the heart of great Moses, such troublesome doubts as there are now in your heart, my son."

Then Boaz went away from before the High Priest and stood alone on the edge of the feasting multitude of men and women; and he considered the words of the High Priest. And Boaz knew then that like Moses he would continue to stand all his life before the thick darkness wherein dwells the Lord of all creation, seeking that knowledge of good and evil which since the beginning has been difficult and painful to man; persisting in that search which sometimes destroys the seeker, but which is yet man's only way to true life.

And Naomi, seeing that Boaz stood alone, took Ruth aside from among the maidens of Shiloh and said: "Boaz is standing alone by himself. Go now near to him that he may look upon you with favor and speak to you."

Ruth said: "Boaz has looked upon me from afar. If it is with favor then let him come to me here and speak to me."

And Naomi said: "The women of Israel have not been too fearful nor too proud to take steps when their men would not act."

Ruth said: "It is not fear that prevents me nor even pride. It is only that I know not what is in the heart of Boaz."

And Naomi said bitterly: "Well, neither does he."

And as they spoke together they saw Reba, led by her father Tobias, approach near to Boaz and speak to him.

But Boaz, seeing then that Ruth had gone apart from the maidens of Shiloh, left off speaking to Reba and Tobias and he turned away from them and went to where Ruth stood alone—for Naomi left her when she saw Boaz approaching.

Boaz said: "Peace unto you."

And Ruth answered him: "Unto you peace."

And he said to her: "Shall I bring you some of the sacrificial meat, Ruth?"

She said: "I have eaten and am satisfied, Boaz; and it has been pleasant to come here as one of the children of Israel assembled before the Lord God of Israel."

"And has our way with our God seemed strange to you?" he said.

And she answered: "Only in that the women stand apart from the men, before the Lord God of Israel."

And he said: "That is done lest the beauty of the women

distract the minds and hearts of the men from the service of the Lord; for ours is a jealous God."

"And has he no love," she said, "for that beauty which is his own creation?"

Boaz said: "Indeed the Lord is a lover of beauty. For again and again the children of Israel were admonished by Moses to make this tabernacle and its service as the Lord had commanded him: *for glory and for beauty*. And Bezalel of Judah gathered all the men who were cunning to work in gold and silver and brass, in cutting stones and carving wood to that end, and the women for weaving."

Ruth looked upon Boaz as he spoke, upon his grave gray eyes and his raven-black hair glinting red where it curled on his head and beard; and her flesh fainted with longing for his beauty and his strength; and Ruth said: "Indeed it is beautiful and glorious," and she turned her dark eyes away to look again upon the tabernacle of acacia gleaming with gold and silver, rising from its forecourt of richly woven curtains.

And she said: "Then it was not the Lord who commanded that the men and the women be parted when they came to worship before him."

Boaz said: "No, it was not. It is the men of Israel who have so ordained it."

And Ruth said: "And it seems to me that men in their fearful zeal sometimes set restraints upon themselves which prevent them not only from doing what is evil but also what is good. And that is why women feel obliged sometimes to break the laws men make."

Boaz said: "And is it then easy for you to know what is evil and what is good?"

And Ruth returned the gaze of his grave gray eyes saying: "Indeed I have always known what is good from what is evil."

200

And he said: "But how?"

And she said: "My heart tells me."

And he said: "But does your heart also give you the reason?"

And looking away from him again she said: "Nay, Boaz, nor do I ask that of my heart. Only men must have reasons—even for their love. And this Naomi has taught me in telling me the tale of Isaac and Rebekah and their two sons Jacob and Esau as it is told in your Book of Remembrance which says: *Now Isaac loved Esau, because he did eat of his venison: and Rebekah loved Jacob.* Rebekah needed no reason."

Then Boaz, smiling upon her, said: "And you need no reason for your love—only that your heart tells you—your heart which knows well what is good."

Ruth said softly: "Indeed it is so, Boaz."

And Boaz said gently: "While I, being but a man, needs must have my reasons. Like the Lord I love what is glorious and beautiful." And he looked with longing upon her lovely face, and said: "And you, Ruth, are——" But there Boaz ceased speaking; for Elias and Gibbor had suddenly appeared beside him, having come to him in great haste.

And Elias took Boaz aside saying urgently: "Word has come, Boaz, that a band of Moabite marauders has been seen on the road south of Bethel."

Then Boaz turned away from Ruth and he said to Gibbor: "Bring me Yohfe;" and to Elias he said: "Sound the alarum!" And Elias took the trumpet and blew a long harsh blast which stilled the singing and laughter of the people, who turned to listen. And Boaz mounted upon Yohfe and spoke to the people saying: "There is a band of Moabites on the road southward, and those of us who go southward must depart at once lest we be overtaken by nightfall and waylaid by an ambush before we arrive at

Bethlehem, and lest they set upon Bethlehem in our absence. Let us therefore depart at once, riding in a close column, the women in the middle of the road with the men surrounding them riding on the right and the left, before and behind them. And all men will carry their weapons in readiness."

And so all those going southward, all those of Judah and Benjamin, mounted their donkeys, horses and their camels and set forth on the road in the manner which Boaz advised; and Boaz on Yohfe rode watchfully at the head of the throng with Gibbor and Elias on either side of him. The eyes of Boaz were fixed on the road ahead and the eyes of Gibbor and Elias were fixed on either side of the road. And thus the throng rode southward past Bethel and Ramah and at noon they came again to Gibeah.

And there the men of Benjamin seeing their opportunity came to Boaz and said: "It is a long time to wait until the wine harvest in Ephraim; so if the men of Judah will give us now their daughters for wives we will continue with you on the road and aid you should you meet the Moabites." And Boaz spoke with the men of Judah. But they said, "We will not break the oath of our fathers who said: *Cursed be he that gives a wife to Benjamin.*" So Boaz said to the men of Benjamin: "You cannot have wives of the daughters of Judah. Wait until the wine harvest and take yourselves wives of the maidens of Shiloh as Gibbor has told you."

But the men of Benjamin said in anger that they wanted wives now and would not continue on the road with the men of Judah who denied them their daughters. So they remained at Gibeah, all but Gibbor who remained beside Boaz, and the throng went on without them, more anxious

202

now because they lacked the help of the strong men of Benjamin.

And Ruth and Naomi riding among the women of Bethlehem heard murmured talk of some spy who had doubtless informed the Moabites of this chance to waylay the people of Bethlehem. And Naomi was very angry as she sat spinning her whorl upon her dove-gray donkey; and Ruth was sad as she rode her milk-white one; but neither one spoke: nor did anyone speak to either of them.

And the throng rode southward unmolested and came unharmed to Jerusalem, the city of the Jebusites. And there outside the walls a troupe of traveling storytellers were setting up their play between two of the buttresses of the great wall; and they said they had just come up from Bethlehem and had seen no sign of any Moabite ma-rauders, neither at Bethlehem nor on the way. So it ap-peared to Boaz that the Moabites, for fear of the returning men of Judah, had gone out of Israel and returned over Jordan to Moab.

And it was the same troupe that Ruth and Naomi had seen there on their way up to Bethlehem, and it was the same story they were going to tell—the story of Samson and Delilah. And Elias urged Boaz to stop for the play, since there was no longer the danger of the Moabites to hasten them homeward, and since most of the women in the throng wished to see it and most of the men would do well to be instructed by the fate of Samson. So Boaz asked the people if they wished to stay for the story, and since most of them did the throng halted there.

But Naomi, incensed at the women who had whispered of a spy among them, and knowing that the story of Samson and Delilah would do the cause of Ruth no good in their eyes, Naomi turned to Ruth and said: "We have seen this before so let us be going on to Bethlehem since there is now no danger." And they turned their donkeys southward and rode away unobserved by the people engrossed in the players.

Now the Jebusites were, as was their wont, gathering on the great wall of the city to look down on the play. And hidden among them so as to be unseen by the Israelites below were some of the Moabite marauders who had taken refuge in the Jebusite city when they spied the approaching Israelites. And among the Moabites hidden behind the Jebusites on the wall were the two burly brothers, the twin princes of the City of Moab.

And looking down from behind the backs of the Jebusites one of these two spied Naomi in the throng of Israelites below who were halting to watch the players. And this one said: "See there that old woman on the gray donkey, is not that the old witch of Judah who sent us on a wild-goose chase along the Salt Sea searching for our Ruth?"

The other said: "Indeed it is she; and that is our Ruth beside her—that one with the golden earrings riding the white donkey."

And the first one said: "That is indeed our Ruth, though she no longer wears the amulets of Ashtar which the daughters of princes in Moab wear."

And the second said: "Behold they two are leaving the throng and going their way alone, along the road to Bethlehem."

And they watched the two women ride southward until at a turn in the road they went out of sight. Then said one of the Moabites to the other: "Let us go out of the city by the farther gate—the Gate of the Fountain—the Israelites watching their play will not heed us; and we will ride around the hills to cut off this turn of the road and then we will overtake the women. We will kill the old witch; and take our Ruth back with us."

So the two descended from the wall and mounted their camels and rode stealthily out of the Gate of the Fountain; and they would have got away from the city unseen were it not for the watchful eyes of Boaz who, ever mindful of the welfare of his people, was riding on Yohfe to and fro about the walls of the city while they were engrossed in the storytellers. And he caught sight of the two Moabites riding swiftly away; and Boaz called Elias and Gibbor to him and said: "I have seen two Moabite marauders riding southward out of the Gate of the Fountain. I am going after them. Do you stay here and prepare the men to guard the women, and to attack any others who may attempt to come out of the city."

Then Boaz spurred Yohfe and rode away in the direction the two Moabites had taken. And though their camels were swift, Yohfe was swifter still and he overtook them as they came to the road where they intended to turn and go after the two women who were out of sight, riding southward and still unmindful of their pursuers.

And there, spear in hand, Boaz rode upon the two Moabites when they turned their evil and hateful faces toward him, and engaged them in fierce fighting. The two men of Moab were very strong and they drew their curved swords and pressed hard upon Boaz but he was very shrewd and nimble in parrying their blows, in separating them by distracting one with a feint while attacking the other, and in eluding their combined attack from both sides thus leaving them snarled in each other's weapons and in conflict with each other. And Boaz, elated, smote them again and again with his spear as Yohfe, neighing with furious delight, reared up over their enraged camels and kicked at them with his sharp hoofs and pranced nimbly about them as they thrust their great swords at Boaz shouting: "We will destroy you and we will take back Ruth the Moabitess!"

And the blood of Boaz ran hot with vengeful anger as he cried: "You shall not have her!" And wild cries of triumph burst from his throat as he smote their swords from the hands of the twin brothers, first one and then the other, circling about them, as if he and the eager beast he bestrode were one. And the wild light of triumph blazed in the eyes of Boaz when he saw the blood spurting from them as he ran them through with his spear, first one and then the other, dragging them down, each one off his camel, and trampling them under the prancing hoofs of Yohfe until the twin princes of Moab lay dead by the roadside.

Then with the taste of victory wild and sweet in his mouth Boaz turned Yohfe and rode swiftly back to Jerusalem. And when he came to the city he saw that many more Jebusites had assembled upon the walls waving weapons and stones, howling and jeering, and threatening the Israelites who stood at bay, massed in the road below, the women to one side guarded by the men who stood between them and the city wall.

And when Boaz rejoined them there rose up a great shout of welcome from the sorely distressed men of Judah. And Elias said with relief: "We feared you had been destroyed by the Moabites."

Boaz said: "I have destroyed them both. Have the Jebusites harmed any one?"

"They threw stones down upon the players and put a stop to their story but have hurt no one yet," said Elias, "but the Moabites among them have been urging them on to attack us, crying that we want to despoil them of their women and shouting that we have taken a woman away from Moab."

And Boaz looked where the women of Israel were gathered and he saw that Ruth was not there among them.

Elias said: "The Moabitess is gone from among us, and so is Naomi. It is possible that the spying Moabitess took Naomi with her into the city to take shelter with her people after the two men of Moab came out of the gate. There are many more Moabites within."

Boaz said nothing.

Then Elias said bitterly: "Perhaps you will agree now that it would have been wiser to have kept her out of our congregation."

Boaz said: "Perhaps."

And Gibbor who had come to them said: "Perhaps you regret now that you did not take her when you could—or at least let me have her."

Elias said: "And should we find her again and lay hands upon her, do not forget that you said she should be stoned for spying."

Boaz cried out: "Be still, both of you!" And he looked up to the walls of Jerusalem whose top was crowded with howling Jebusites and Moabites.

Then Gibbor said angrily: "Well, Boaz, shall we try to depart now? If we but turn our backs on them to go they will surely attack us from the walls and others will come out of the gates to pursue us. Let us attack them now, suddenly, and have done with them once and for all and let us indeed take their women, all of them this time."

Boaz said: "Let us not concern ourselves now with their

women but with our own who must be saved. But you are right, Gibbor, in saying we must attack them before we can get away. This is not how I thought to spend this day when we set out peacefully for Shiloh to give thanks to the Lord God of Israel. I had not thought to have killed two men with my hands and to engage in battle with a host. But surely the Lord will be with us in this hour. Blow your trumpet, Elias!"

And when Elias had blown a loud blast on his ram's horn, Boaz spoke to the men and women of Judah saying: "We must needs fight the Jebusites and the Moabites with them before we can return to our homes in peace. And now I shall say to you as Moses said to the children of Israel before they came into this land: *When thou goest forth to battle against thine enemies and seest a people more than thou, thou shalt not be afraid of them: for the Lord thy God is with thee, which brought thee up out of the land of Egypt. And Moses said, Hear, O Israel, ye draw nigh this day unto battle against your enemies: let not your heart faint; fear not, nor tremble, neither be ye affrighted at them; for the Lord your God is he that goeth with you to fight for you against your enemies, to save you! And Moses said: What man is there that hath betrothed a wife, and hath not yet taken her? Let him go and return unto his house, lest he die in battle*—so I say now: Let those who were married this day at Shiloh leave the ranks of the men and withdraw with the women to a safe distance as we go to attack." And Boaz waited until the newly married men took their places with the women.

Then he continued: "And I say to you now as Moses said: *What man is there that is fearful and fainthearted? Let him go and return unto his house, lest his brethren's*

208

heart melt as his heart." And he waited again until the elderly men like Tobias, who took the reluctant boy Joel with him, went aside also among the women.

Then Boaz divided the remaining men into three parts, one to follow Elias in guarding the Gate of Gihon, one to follow Gibbor in guarding the Gate of the Fountain and one to follow Boaz himself in storming the walls. These last were the sharp-eyed archers and the fleet climbers.

And when he had done with dividing the men he said: "And now I remind you of what the Lord said to Joshua: *There shall not any man be able to stand before thee all the days of thy life; as I was with Moses, so I will be with thee: I will not fail thee, nor forsake thee. Be strong and of a good courage!* And see there," cried Boaz pointing northward toward Shiloh, "comes help from the Lord!"

The people turned and looked, and in the northern sky a black cloud was rising fast and approaching with the wind from the north; and as they looked it was rent by a stroke of lightning.

And Boaz turned and went toward the city wall and shouted up to the Jebusites: "Moses, our leader, who brought us up out of Egypt commanded us: *When thou drawest nigh unto a city to fight against it, then proclaim peace unto it.* So I ask you, O Jebusites, shall we have peace?" And they answered him with jeers and a shower of stones and one of the stones grazed his head and drew blood.

Then Boaz shouted to the men of Israel. And Elias and his men ran to the Gate of Gihon, and Gibbor and his men ran to the Fountain Gate, and the archers, shouting *Hallelujah!* let loose a rain of arrows that swept the top of the wall of the Jebusites, and brought many of them tumbling down pierced through and through by the arrows, while Boaz and his followers went clambering up the steep stones. At the city gates the Moabites who attempted to come out were driven back by the spears and swords of the men of Elias and Gibbor. And many were killed at the gates, especially at the Fountain Gate where Gibbor when hard pressed would reach with his left hand for the unexpected sword concealed on his right thigh and hew down a dozen of them. Then the Moabites left the gates and returned back to the walls to help the remaining Jebusites attack the mounting climbers of Boaz. But by then the black cloud from the north had rolled down over the city of Jerusalem and with great rumblings of thunder and blinding flashes of lightning let loose a flood of rain and hail that drove the Moabites with the Jebusites down off the walls and into the shelter of their houses.

So the Israelites picked up their wounded and bound up their wounds and withdrew southward down the road toward Bethlehem and were soon out of the storm, riding again in bright sunshine. . . .

Of all this—of their pursuit by the two Moabites and of the ensuing fight at Jerusalem—Ruth and Naomi knew nothing as they rode southward toward Bethlehem. At first both rode in silence.

Ruth was sadly silent, remembering her joy at having been one with the women of Israel and how Boaz had come close to her of his own accord to speak with her.

And Naomi was angrily silent, remembering how the players of the Samson story had appeared just then when the people's suspicion of Ruth had been stirred by news of the Moabite marauders. But Naomi, though she spun her whorl swiftly as she rode her slow-moving donkey, could not long contain herself. "And what had Boaz been speaking of," she burst out, "when Elias and Gibbor came with the evil news?"

"Of good and evil and of glory and beauty," said Ruth.

"Of your beauty?" asked Naomi.

"Nay," said Ruth, "he told me that the Lord God of Israel is a lover of beauty."

Naomi's face fell: "And did you not ask Boaz if he is a lover of beauty? Did you not get him to say that he loves your beauty? That is what I would have done in your place," and she looked with impatience upon Ruth riding beside her; but Ruth gave her no answer. Then said Naomi more gently: "You missed your chance, my daughter. And you must now learn that there are times when a woman has to lead a man by one way or another into doing what it is his manifest destiny to do. At least that is so among the men of Israel. Why that is so only the Lord God of Israel knows; but the women of Israel have known for a long, long time that it is so. Surely Rebekah knew it when she got blind Isaac to give his blessing to Jacob and not to Esau. And were it not for such a woman in Israel Boaz himself would not be alive today. For this Boaz is descended from Judah out of Tamar who was Judah's own daughter-in-law; and that was not Judah's doing but Tamar's and how that came about I shall tell you as it was told to me: *Now Judah took a wife for Er his first-born, and her name was Tamar. And Er, Judah's first-born, was wicked in the sight of the Lord; and the Lord slew him. And Judah said to Onan, his second son, Go in unto thy brother's wife and perform the duty of an husband's brother unto her, and raise up seed to thy brother.*

And it came to pass when Onan went in unto his brother's wife, that he spilled it on the ground lest he should give seed to his brother. And the thing he did was evil in the sight of the Lord and he slew him also." And there Naomi stopped the story and her spinning to say to Ruth: "Any woman will agree that the Lord God of Israel is a just God."

And Ruth said bitterly: "There was little comfort for Tamar. Is that justice?"

Naomi without heeding Ruth resumed the story and her spinning: *Then said Judah to Tamar his daughter-in-law, Remain a widow in thy father's house, till Shelah my third son be grown up. And Tamar went and dwelt in her father's house. But when Shelah was grown up, she was not given unto him for wife. Now Judah went up to his sheepshearers to Timnah. And it was told Tamar. And she put off her garments of her widowhood, and covered herself with her veil, and wrapped herself, and she covered her face and sat in the gate of Enaim, which is by the way to Timnah. And when Judah saw her, he thought her to be an harlot.* There Naomi stopped her spinning and the story again to say to Ruth: "Now it should be said in Judah's behalf that his wife had died."

And Ruth said: "But is it not curious that men are wont to look down upon the harlot and denounce her temptations though it is their lust and not hers that she serves."

Naomi said: "Indeed that is curious," and then she continued: *And he turned unto her by the way and said, Go to, I pray thee, let me come in unto thee: for he knew not that she was his daughter-in-law. And she said, What wilt thou give me, that thou mayest come in unto me? And he said, I will send thee a kid of the goats from the flock. And she said, Wilt thou give me a pledge, till thou send it? And he said, What pledge shall I give thee?*

And Ruth said: "Yet it seems to me unfair that a woman should take advantage of the urgent lustfulness of a man, as Delilah did to Samson, and Tamar to Judah."

Naomi said: "It depends on the end to be served: Delilah's was evil, Tamar's was—well, now listen to her story which I tell you just as it is told in our Book of Remembrance: *And she said, Thy signet and thy cord, and thy staff that is in thy hand. And he gave them to her, and came in unto her, and she conceived by him. And she arose, and went away, and put off her veil from her, and put on the garments of her widowhood. And Judah sent the kid of the goat by the hand of a friend to receive the pledge from the woman's hand but he found her not. Then he asked the men of the place, saying, Where is the harlot, that was at Enaim by the wayside? And they said, There hath been no harlot here. And he returned to Judah and said, I have not found her. And it came to pass about three months after, that one told Judah, Tamar thy daughter-in-law hath played the harlot; and moreover, behold, she is with child by whoredom. And Judah said, Bring her forth, and let her be burnt.*"

Then Ruth said: "Now is it not curious that men when they are unable to destroy the evil within themselves will then turn with vengeance upon the wrong it has done!"

And Naomi said: "Indeed that is curious also; and this is something a woman must guard herself against as did Tamar: *But when she was brought forth she said, By the man whose these are am I with child; and she said, Discern, I pray thee, whose are these, this signet, and cords, and this staff. And Judah acknowledged them and said, She is more righteous than I; foreasmuch as I gave her not Shelah,*

my son. And it came to pass in the time of her travail
that behold twins were in her womb. And it came to pass
when she travailed, that one put out a hand, and the mid
wife took and bound upon his hand a scarlet thread, saying.
This came out first. And it came to pass, as he drew back
his hand that, behold, his brother came out, and Tamar
said, Wherefore hast thou made a 'breach' for thyself?
Therefore his name is called 'Perez'."

Then Naomi ceased her spinning and she turned to
Ruth and said: *"And Perez begat Hezron, and Hezron*
begat Ram, and Ram begat Aminadab, and Aminadab
begat Nashon, and Nashon begat Salmon, and Salmon
begat Boaz—because Tamar was a determined woman."

"But Tamar did not want the love of Judah," said
Ruth softly, "she wanted only the child. The love of a
man is not to be got by the determined will of a woman."

Then Ruth remained silent a while as they rode on;
until she said: "Whose burial place is that?" pointing
ahead to a single domed tomb by the side of the road.
"I observed it as we went by on the Passover night when
we first came to Bethlehem; and again on our way up to
Shiloh. It is a lonely grave."

"That," said Naomi, "is the tomb of Rachel, the dearly
beloved wife of Jacob. Now there was a man who knew
what he wanted! He wanted Rachel, and he did not rest
until he had got her. But she died here by the roadside in
childbirth when Jacob returned from Haran where he
met and married her." Then Naomi said: "And that is
one thing in which I hold that the Creator of the universe
has been unjust: that the man does not risk his life in the
creation of his children while the woman does. It is a man's
God. And it is a man's world," she added bitterly. "For
all our scheming they do things in their own good time.
Though we bring them into the world in pain, they leave

214

our wombs and go their own ways. That you have yet to learn, my daughter—and it will make another woman of you."

Ruth said: "I have learned much from thee, Naomi. And I am already another woman; I am no longer Ruth the Moabitess but Ruth the woman of Israel though I am still suspect in Israel."

And when they came to the door of the tomb Ruth said: "Let us halt here;" so they dismounted and tethered their donkeys and went into the tomb. And in the low vaulted room there were memorial lamps burning above the mound of masonry over the long-buried body; and on the grave there were many pieces of parchment and clay tablets upon which were inscribed petitions addressed to Mother Rachel.

And Naomi said: "These petitions are brought here and the lamps kept alight by barren women; for Rachel was long barren before she bore Jacob a son."

"But," said Ruth, "is not this like the magic which women in Moab practise when they wear the charms of fertile Ashtar?"

"Indeed," said Naomi, "it is. And until men find them a surer way to make them fertile, barren women will try any means to that end. Rachel said it was some mandrakes she had got from her sister Leah; and when her first child was born she called him 'Joseph' saying, The Lord 'add' to me another—so eager was she to bear her beloved Jacob still another son. And it was in bearing Benjamin that she died here on the way."

Then Ruth said: "Any woman willingly risks death in bearing a child for the man she loves, and even more so for the man who loves her dearly; and thou didst say that Rachel was the dearly beloved wife of Jacob."

And Naomi said, "Surely he loved her greatly, from the

moment he first saw her at the well in Haran where she came to water her father's sheep. And when Laban her father asked Jacob what wages he wanted for his service Jacob answered, *I shall serve thee seven years for Rachel, thy young daughter,* and Jacob served Laban seven years for Rachel, and it is said that *they seemed unto him but a few days, for the love he had for her.* But when the time came for the marriage Laban deceived Jacob by putting Leah his elder, ill-favored daughter in her place. And though Laban also gave him Zilpah for a handmaid, Jacob willingly served Laban yet another seven years for Rachel. And though he got from Laban Bilhah also for a handmaid and though Jacob begat ten sons with Leah and Zilpah and Bilhah, and though Rachel was long barren before she bore Joseph and then died here bearing Benjamin, it was Rachel alone that Jacob loved to the end."

And Ruth said, "It is thus that I long to be loved and wanted by the man whose sons I shall bear."

"But do not think," said Naomi, "that it was easy for Rachel to live with such a man as Jacob, for all his love. For our father Israel was like so many of his sons, of whom I have spoken—like my Elimelech and like this Boaz whom you love—a thoughtful man, restless in mind, gentle and never violent, yet wrestling with God and with men. You have heard how this dreamer Jacob made a bargain with God Almighty at Bethel. Any other man, having got what he wanted, would have been content to remain in peace in Haran serving his father-in-law who had been generous to him. But no, Jacob must return here and struggle with his violent brother Esau, and make of his people a nation to serve the Lord God of Israel. And Rachel had to steal her father's gods and deceive him to save the life of Jacob from her father's wrath; and Rachel who might have lived in ease in her father's house in Haran had to lose her life on the way, bearing another son to Jacob."

"Nevertheless," said Ruth, "do I envy Rachel, even her death in childbirth, here by the roadside; for she was dearly beloved." And she went and bowed herself down by the tomb, and prayed in silence to Rachel to intercede for her with Almighty God for the love of Boaz. Then Ruth leaned her head against the tomb of Rachel and wept. . . .

Now as the men and women of Judah rode homeward after the fight at Jerusalem, though some of the men had suffered injuries and bore wounds, all of them rejoiced in their deliverance from the hands of the Jebusites and the Moabites. And Gibbor and his troupe of young men riding behind them as a rear guard sang songs of victory. They sang the song of Moses and Miriam:

> *The Lord is a man of war:*
> *The Lord is his name.*
> *Pharaoh's chariots and his host he cast into the sea:*
> *And his captains are sunk in the Red Sea,*
> *The deeps cover them:*
> *They went down in the depths like a stone. . . .*

And Zvuv rode up and down the column shouting exultantly: *Prove me now herewith, saith the Lord, heed my commandments and I will pour you out a blessing that there shall not be room enough to receive it. And I will rebuke the devourer for your sakes, and he shall not take nor destroy the fruits of your ground. And all nations shall*

217

call you happy: for ye shall be a delightful land, saith the Lord. . . .

And Boaz, the wound on his head bound up, rode with Elias before the throng, Boaz on coppery Yohfe and Elias on his snow-white mare. But Boaz was no longer elated. Vigilantly he scanned the road and watched both sides of it.

And they two spurred their horses and rode on ahead. And so they two came before all the rest to where Boaz had left the two Moabites he had slain. And Boaz and Elias stopped there and dismounted to take the two bloody bodies away from the roadside where they would become an evil stench to travelers.

And Elias said to Boaz as they bore away the dead bodies: "Why does it not rejoice you now, Boaz, that you have slain these two Moabites and have delivered your people this day out of the hands of their enemies?"

Boaz said: "When I fought and killed these two men of Moab I was indeed elated. Then I and Yohfe were as one beast. He neighed and I shouted in triumph. But I am a lover of peace and I hate in my inmost heart the destruction of the life of mankind. And the Lord God of Israel has instructed us in his covenant to commit no murder."

And Elias said: "But has not the Lord God of Israel instructed us to destroy our enemies and did he not this very day come to our aid when we turned and attacked them?"

And Boaz said: "Yet the Lord God of Israel is a lover of peace. Is not the Lord's blessing that he shall *lift up his countenance upon thee, and give thee peace*? And do we not greet each other with 'Peace'?"

Elias said: "Indeed it is well that we should greet our own brothers with peace and should live in peace with them. But surely it is vain to look for peace with such men as these." And he pushed the two bodies so that they rolled down into a deep ditch where the vultures and wild beasts would soon devour them.

And Boaz looked down upon the faces of the dead men and said: "Yet we are told that God said to Cain: *At the hand of man, even at the hand of every man's brother, will I require the life of man. Whoso sheddeth man's blood, by man shall his blood be shed; for in the image of God made he man.*"

"But not those Moabites!" said Elias and he spat down upon them.

And Boaz said: "Even those Moabites. For is not the Lord our God the creator of us all? Did he not make Cain as well as Abel? And was not Esau, who was the father of Edom, the brother of Jacob our father?"

Elias said: "But the Lord our God has seen fit to harden the evil hearts of some men and these we must destroy without mercy, lest we ourselves be destroyed by them or by the evil that is in them."

And Boaz said: "Evil though our enemies may be, nevertheless it troubles me that among the nations it will be said of Israel that we also have slain many men to gain our land."

Elias said: "Even Moses, who knew God's will better than any man and was himself the meekest of men, smote an Egyptian and killed him in righteous anger. Let those nations which have not slaughtered others even for a righteous cause chide the children of Israel for the dead they have made in Canaan. And the Lord God of Israel himself has been as troubled in spirit as you are, Boaz, about this business. Did he not once destroy all of mankind on the earth saving only Noah and his house?"

Then Boaz and Elias returned to the road and rejoined the people of Judah who were rejoicing in song and in laughter as they rode. And they cried out when they saw Boaz: "Hail Boaz, our hero and our judge!"

And Zvuv came to Boaz and said: "The young men have sent me to speak to you of what seems to them wise and to all the rest of the people also, for we have asked them."

And Boaz said: "Tell me what the men have in mind."

Zvuv said: "They say that Israel has need of a king to unite the tribes, to strengthen each one by binding them all together. Had you been king at Shiloh you could have said not only to the men of Benjamin but to all of the other tribes, come continue with us on this journey lest we meet with the Moabites, and we should surely have been spared this attack."

And Elias said eagerly: "That is indeed a wise thought, Boaz. Israel has need of a king. And did not Jacob in his blessing of Judah say: *The sceptre shall not depart from Judah, nor the ruler's staff from between his feet, till he come to Shiloh, having the obedience of the people.* And who in Judah is better fitted than you, Boaz? At the feast of tabernacles we will call an assembly of all the tribes at Shiloh and surely they will agree and the High Priest will anoint you then and there."

And Boaz said: "Bring the people to a halt."

So Elias raised his ram's horn to his lips and blew a blast that brought the people to a halt. And they cried again: "Hail, Boaz!" as he turned and faced them, sitting on Yohfe before them.

And Boaz said to them: "It has been told me that you

220

are asking for a king. Have you forgotten how Abimelech, son of Gideon, who made himself king slew not only his brothers but all of the city of Shechem which he laid in ruins? Why do you want a king?"

And some cried out: "To bind us together, to make us strong." And others shouted: "To lead us in time of need; to go out before us against our enemies and fight our battles." And the farmers cried: "To protect our crops and our cattle." And Tobias spoke for the merchants saying: "To protect our caravans and put the thieving marauders to flight. . . ."

When they had all ceased speaking Boaz said: "You are free men and strong and the strength of the Lord God of Israel is with you so long as you live according to his commandment which he has given you. It is when men do evil and forego the strength of righteousness that they lose heart in themselves and give up the freedom which they have corrupted, seeking in a king the strength they should have in themselves. But kings, feeling their powers, become tyrants. And a king will take your sons for his army and your daughters for his handmaidens, and he will tax you and take the tenth of your flocks and your grains, and you will serve him and you will fight his battles whether you will or no. And it shall no longer be said that there is no king in Israel and every man does what is right in his own eyes."

Still the people raised up their voices and said: "But we will have a king over us, that we also may be like all the nations." And they shouted again: "Hail, Boaz!"

But Boaz shook his head and silenced them saying: "The kings of Moab and Ammon and the other nations hold their peoples in swinish subjection to themselves and their abominable gods. The Lord God of Israel has said: *Ye shall be a peculiar treasure unto me.* And I say as Gideon said: *I will not rule over you, neither shall my son rule over you. The Lord shall rule over you.*" And Boaz turned the head of Yohfe his horse and rode southward again before all the people of Judah, who were grieved that he had refused them their wish for a king.

And when they approached the tomb of Rachel by the roadside Ruth and Naomi were coming out of the tomb. And the boy, Joel, spurred his donkey and hastened ahead, eager to tell Ruth all that had occurred. Breathlessly he said: "There were many Moabites with the Jebusites within the city and two of them, enormous twin princes, came out of the city and they might have pursued you and killed you but Boaz went after them and overtook them and killed them both and then he returned to Jerusalem and led the fierce fight against the Jebusites and the Moabites on the walls, who threatened us with stones and spears and you should have seen Boaz, he fought like a lion and I saw him kill three of the Jebusites at a time, and we defeated them all with the help of the Lord who sent a wind from the north, from Shiloh, with a hail storm from heaven that was like the seventh plague in Egypt, and I fought with my sling as you showed me and I killed many of the enemy. So now you are safe. And after the battle we all wanted Boaz to become King of Israel, but he would not."

Ruth raised her dark eyes to look upon Boaz as he approached, and she saw the wound on his head and was grieved; but he did not return her gaze, though he said to Elias riding beside him: "You see, you were wrong: she did not go into Jerusalem. Were she guilty of spying and treachery she would not be here."

And cool-eyed Elias said: "Nevertheless, was she not in

good part the cause of those Moabites coming upon us?"

And when Ruth and Naomi rejoined the throng on its way to Bethlehem none other than the lad Joel greeted Ruth or spoke to her; not one of the young men who had clustered about her on the journey northward came near to her. For Zvuv went among them crying aloud for all to hear: "Remember Samson!

> *The mouth of a strange woman is a deep pit.*
> *He that is against the Lord shall fall into it."*

So the young men turned aside from Ruth. And Naomi was very angry and left Ruth and went to ride behind Zvuv saying: *"Whoso keepeth his mouth and his tongue keepeth his soul from trouble."*

But Zvuv gave her no heed and shouted louder to the young men:

> *Heed thyself from the strange woman,*
> *Even from the alien woman*
>   *that maketh smooth her words. . . .*
> *For her house sinketh down unto death*
> *And her paths unto the shades;*
> *None that go unto her return,*
> *Neither do they attain*
>   *unto the paths of life. . . .*

And Naomi said to him: "Rachel and Leah, the wives of Jacob the father of all Israel, were from Haran—daughters of Laban who worshipped teraphim."

But Zvuv ignored her and shouted: *Samson profaned the holiness of the Lord and married the daughter of a strange god. The Lord will cut off the man who does this!*

And Naomi said: "Yet Moses married Zipporah, daughter of a priest of Midian."

Then Zvuv turned and answered her saying: "But that

223

was before he brought down our laws. A man who learns the error of his own way becomes the best teacher of others."

Naomi answered: "Yet later Moses married a Cushite."

And Zvuv, ignoring her again, lifted up his voice so that even Boaz riding ahead with Elias would hear him. "And Moses said: *An Ammonite or a Moabite shall not enter into the assembly of the Lord!*"

And Elias said to Boaz: "Who knows but that this woman of Moab was indeed sent by those marauders to spy us out for them."

Boaz looked back and saw Ruth riding alone, her head held high but sadness dimming her dark eyes. And he said, "Be still, Elias. She is a stranger among us."

And Naomi cried out in great bitterness to the people: "Moses said: *He doth execute the judgment of the fatherless and the widow, and loveth the stranger, giving him food and raiment. Love ye therefore the stranger; for we were strangers in the land of Egypt.* And Moses said: *A stranger shalt thou not wrong, neither shalt thou oppress him; for ye were strangers in the land, of Egypt.* And again Moses said: *A stranger shalt thou not oppress; for ye know the heart of a stranger, seeing that ye were strangers in the land of Egypt.*" Then she ceased speaking and went to ride beside Ruth.

And Naomi turned her donkey and Ruth's to ride near to Boaz; but as they approached him, the rich matron of Bethlehem whom Naomi had affronted in the market place came riding close to Boaz with her two bedizened daughters and she said to him: "Dear brave Boaz, how you must want a respite from the rude life you live with those crude men in the fields! Do come to us tonight and let me and my Sara and Hannah make you

224

a savory meal. Sara would cook whatever you wish and Hannah would be most happy to serve you, Boaz—would you not, my daughters?"

But Boaz answered her brusquely saying, "We have yet to winnow the last of the barley and I shall eat and sleep with my men tonight on the threshing floor. Come, Elias, let us hasten ahead and see that all is well in the city before the rest enter." For they were approaching the gates of Bethlehem. So Boaz spurred his horse Yohfe and galloped away into the city.

Then cunning Tobias the merchant, seeing that the market for what he wanted had fallen, guided his camel so as to ride beside Naomi and murmured to her so that Ruth would not hear him, saying that he was ready, despite what was said of the Moabitess, to take Ruth into his household and, he added: "I will give you a little something for the land."

Whereupon Naomi turned to Ruth and said: "Tobias wants you, Ruth."

And Ruth said gently: "But I do not love thee, Tobias. And I will marry only the man whom I love."

"Love!" said Tobias disdainfully. "I am not speaking of that foolish, childish business! Nor of marriage! Do you think anyone here will marry you?"

Ruth said: "Then I shall marry no one, and shall live alone."

And Tobias said angrily: "We do not ask damsels here what they will do!"

Then Naomi said: "Moses said of the five daughters of Zelophehad, when their father died in the desert, *Let them marry whom they think best.*"

And Tobias cried: "Then will you not give her to me, Naomi?"

And Naomi said: "The sages say:

> *Three sorts of men my soul hateth;*
> *And their ways greatly offend me:*
> *A poor man that is haughty*
> *A rich man that is a liar,*
> *And an old man that is a lecher lacking understanding.*

Go on, you old goat!" cried Naomi, and she gave the legs of his camel a switch that sent it galloping.

BUT WHEN THEY came home at sunset Naomi was sorely troubled and fretful. And she said bitterly to Ruth: "My Elimelech when he had got what he wanted used to say very sagely:

Hope deferred maketh the heart sick;
But desire fulfilled is a tree of life.

But how in this world of men a woman can get *her* desire fulfilled he did not say."

And Ruth stopped in the open doorway to gaze upon the full moon rising above the long misty blood-red line of the distant mountains of Moab which were sinking down into darkness. And she thought with loathing of the abominations of the high place in the city of Moab; and she thought with longing of the glory of the tabernacle of the Lord God of Israel and of Boaz and the men of Israel dancing before the altar of the Lord; and she thought of the drunken princes of Moab who came down from the high place and had taken up Orpah; and she thought of the fearful suspicion of the men and women of Israel of the stranger sojourning among them; and again of the grave gray eyes of Boaz and his raven-black hair with glints of red where it curled on his head and beard. And she knew he would never take her, though she yearned for him, for his strong body and his exalted spirit, with all the awakened womanhood of her body and spirit. And it was in Ruth's heavy heart to say to Naomi: "Would it not be better for us both if I returned now to the house of my mother in Moab?"

But before she could turn and lift up her voice, Naomi said sharply to Ruth: "It is no good your looking back there. Remember what happened to Lot's wife." And she set about lighting the lamps.

And Ruth said: "I have no wish to return to Moab. Did I not say to thee: Thy people shall be my people? And now that I love Boaz, even though thy people do not welcome me, I would gladly cleave to him here even as thou didst cleave to Elimelech in Moab." And her sweet voice turned bitter as she said: "But if Boaz does not want me——" and shrugging her shoulders she ceased speaking.

Naomi said: "It is all very well at your age to say, 'Then I shall marry no one'; but when you are as old as I am you will wish sometimes in your loneliness that you had married anyone, as I sometimes wish I had—even a Moabite." Then, herself disconsolate, the weary old woman sat and watched Ruth go about the household, setting in order what was disarrayed, preparing their meager meal. "And now," said Naomi, "now that the barley harvest is over it will not be easy to provide for our needs; and you will sit here with me, poor and alone, wasting your youth and your beauty."

Then Ruth came and stood before her. "Wouldst thou have me go to Tobias?" she said.

And fire flared up in those old eyes. "Surely not!" said Naomi.

"Well?" said Ruth, and smiled sadly down upon her.

The fire in Naomi's eyes turned into a light: "Boaz loves you," she said. "I have known in my time the look of love in a man's eyes; and surely I saw it shine in the eyes of Boaz when he gazed upon you all the way up to Shiloh, and there before the tabernacle."

"Well then?" said Ruth without hope.

"Well, then let him say so," said Naomi; "let him say that he wants you for his wife."

"Well, then let him," said Ruth dubiously.

"Then make him!" whispered Naomi.

"But how?" said Ruth.

And Naomi said: "Listen, my daughter. Boaz is winnowing barley; and tonight with his men he will sleep on the threshing floor. See down there in the field they are lighting the fires for the evening meal." She pointed through the open door. "And they will feast and drink well tonight because of the victory over the Jebusites. Listen to them!" And the voices of the men, their talk and loud laughter rose up from the valley, and the song the winnowers sang as they threshed in the rising moonlight:

> *There are threescore queens,*
>   *And fourscore concubines,*
>   *And virgins without number.*
> *But my dove, my undefiled is one,*
>   *The only one of her mother. . . .*

And Naomi said to Ruth: "Do you now bathe and anoint yourself sweetly and go down to the field and wait until Boaz has eaten and drunk and his heart is merry, and watch where he lies down to sleep. Then go and lie down at his feet." A ringing shout rose up from the men in the field below. "He will tell you what you shall do," said Naomi.

And Ruth looked long into the wise old eyes of Naomi, but said nothing.

Naomi said: "Boaz, like Tobias, is our near kinsman

and he has the right to redeem the land of Elimelech. Though it would not be truly a levirate marriage."

Still Ruth stood silent.

And Naomi continued speaking and said: "When Zelophehad of the tribe of Manasseh died in the wilderness and left no sons, his five daughters came to Moses and asked for his inheritance and Moses ordained then that if a man died without leaving a son his daughter might inherit. And you, my daughter, have been better to me than seven sons and are the true inheritor of Elimelech. And Moses then said concerning the daughters of Zelophehad: *Let them marry to whom they think best; only to the family of the tribe of their father shall they marry. So shall no inheritance of the children of Israel remove from tribe to tribe.* And though it is true that your father is of Moab and not of Judah, still, if you marry Boaz, the inheritance of Elimelech will remain in the tribe of Judah."

And Ruth said: "That is most shrewdly said, Naomi." But then Ruth remained silent before her.

Naomi said: "You are in your heart a true woman of Israel else would you not have come away with me from Moab and I would not urge you now to enter into the congregation of the Lord. And although in Israel obedience to the ancient laws is enjoined, yet are the breachmakers not without honor; like the younger son who goes before his elder brother as did Perez, forefather of Boaz, and like that determined woman Tamar who bore him, but for whose determination Boaz himself would not now be here; and like all those other determined women in Israel, homeborn and stranger alike, of whom I have told you."

And Ruth said: "Indeed I remember them well—all the women of whom thou hast told me: Sarah who laughed in the face of the angel of the Lord; and Rebekah who deceived Isaac her blind husband for the sake of her son Jacob; and Rachel who stole the gods of Laban her father for the sake of her husband Jacob; and Zipporah who saved the life of Moses from before the wrath of the Lord; and Deborah who led all Israel to victory; and Jael who killed Sisera. All those were valiant women, to be sure. But none of them went to offer herself to the man she loved—not even Tamar."

And seeing that Ruth remained standing still as if unmoved, Naomi said sharply: "In Israel where there is yet no king and every man does what is right in his own eyes, shall not a woman do likewise?"

Still Ruth said nothing. And in the silence between them they heard shouts of loud male laughter rising up from the fire-and-moonlit field of Boaz.

Then Ruth said softly: "Art thou indeed certain, Naomi, that Boaz loves me?"

And Naomi said: "Indeed I am certain!"

Then Ruth smiled suddenly and she said: "I will do as thou sayest, Naomi. And it will be for thy sake as well as for mine."

And Naomi smiled also and said: "Come then, my daughter, and prepare yourself."

And as they heated the water and got ready the basin for the bath, the old woman talked of the stubborn pride and perversity of man which so often made it necessary for women to beguile them into doing the things they needed and indeed wanted to do: "For they are in such fearful doubt about us: *Folly is a woman!* they cry in their proverbs; and yet when they speak of wisdom it is always in the guise of a woman:

> *Say unto Wisdom, Thou art my sister;*
> *And call Understanding thy kinswoman,*
> *That they may keep thee from the strange woman.*

Thus we are to blame for everything—the good and the evil. And then after they get what they want they blame us for tempting them. It has been so from the very beginning," said Naomi as she poured the hot water in with the cold, and Ruth undressed. "It has been so since Adam and Eve. Certainly Adam wanted, as much as Eve did, that knowledge of both good and evil. What man does not? But the story makes it appear that she tempted him to it. It is plainly a man's story; because we know very well that women do not go climbing trees—even for apples. . . ."

And Ruth said: "To me it has seemed a strange story in that the Lord God is said to have placed the tree there in the garden and yet forbid it them and then punished them for eating of it. If the Lord God did not wish them to have it, why then did he put it there?"

And Naomi, baring her elbow and testing the warmth of the water, said: "That, my daughter, shows plainly that it is the story of a thoughtful man troubled by the knowledge that long ago his Almighty Creator gave him the freedom to choose to live either like the ignorant beast which knows not good from evil or like the Lord God himself who knows both, and has the power to do both. For God wants man to do good of his own free will and choosing. And a good woman in helping him to that choice will make him feel he is doing God's will. Now the trouble with men is that they think this thing or that is evil, when the evil lies not in the thing itself but in that which is done with it. Now that knife which my Elimelech made for me is not in itself either good or evil," and she pointed to the knife of sharp flint she had brought from Moab. "But when it cuts my bread it is good; and if I should hatefully kill someone with it then it would be evil. So too with the seductiveness of women which thoughtful men have come to fear because of the power it has over them and the evil use to which it has been put by women like Delilah the Philistine. Torn as men often are between the good and the evil in themselves, they do not understand that a woman is seldom so divided in spirit—that a woman's spirit is indeed more constant and reliable than a man's because she is wholeheartedly either one or the other— good or evil. The woman who uses her beauty to bring a man to his own good and delight is a true woman; and a true woman happily gives herself to the man she loves to that end."

Ruth said: "Gleaning in the field of Boaz I have wondered about women like the contentious wife of Zvuv, who has not given herself happily to Zvuv nor to any man."

"The unhappy daughter of Simeon," said Naomi, "is in her heart no woman and hence she has no influence over her man Zvuv, whether for good or for evil. Our Mother Rachel was a good woman and she used her womanly power even over her father Laban for the sake of her beloved Jacob. Delilah was evil but she was a woman and hence had the power over Samson for evil."

Ruth said: "On the way here from Moab you said of Samson: The strong man's weakness is in his head. Tell me now, Naomi, where is the wise man's weakness? For Boaz' wisdom is even greater than his strength."

And Naomi said: "The wise man's weakness is in his heart. And the doubts which assail the minds of wise and thoughtful men restrain them from action, from doing what needs to be done. It is then that a good woman can help a wise man, by assailing his heart, where lies his weakness. Have no fear; you will move the heart of Boaz. Come now, my daughter, and I shall bathe you, for the water is just right."

And Ruth went and stood naked in the basin of water and Naomi bathed her beautiful young body. And Naomi said: "My Elimelech used to say:

> *The glory of young men is their strength;*
> *And the beauty of old men is their hoary head.*

Now surely one can say: The glory of young women is their beauty. But tell me," she said sadly, "where is the beauty of old women?"

And Ruth said: "The beauty of old women is their wisdom."

And old Naomi, musing upon the loveliness of Ruth, of breasts and belly and thighs, milk white and firm yet silken soft and smooth, said gently: "And to think that I, too, was once as lovely as this! I remember how Elimelech loved to touch me—'Milk and silk,' he used to say, 'Milk and silk!'—and how excited he got, dear Elimelech! . . ." And washing the dust of travel from the shapely feet of Ruth, she said: "But what men do not remember is that time deals more quickly and more harshly with us than with them. Hence a woman may be forgiven if she is impatient for the fulfillment of her desire while she is yet young. The Lord knows that men are urgent enough when their desire is great. Listen to them!"

And from the fire-and-moonlit field of Boaz the strong voices of the men rose up in song:

> *Come, my beloved, let us go forth into the field;*
> *Let us lodge in the villages.*
> *Let us rise up early to the vineyards;*
> *Let us see if the vine hath budded,*
> *And the tender grape appeared,*
> *And the pomegranate be in flower:*

There will I give thee my love.
The mandrakes give forth fragrance,
And at our doors are all manner of precious fruits,
New and old,
Which I have laid up for thee, O my beloved.

And Naomi said: "For all that Zvuv told them on the way to Shiloh about the meaning of that song, it is not for the love of God they are singing now."

Ruth said: "It must be hard for a man to know when he truly loves a woman, since he can lust for a woman whether or not he loves her. A woman has no lust for a man she does not love."

Naomi said: "Indeed it is curious that only when a man loves a woman can he restrain his lust, which then becomes the servant of his love." And as she dried Ruth's body Naomi chanted in her quavering voice:

There be three things too wonderful for me:
Yea, four that I know not:
The way of an eagle in the air;
The way of a serpent upon a rock;
The way of a ship in the midst of the sea;
And the way of a man with a maid.

And Ruth said: "When you first told it to me on the way from Moab, my heart was fearful of that fourth wonder. But now that I love Boaz I want with all my heart to know it."

Naomi said: "Rest assured now, my daughter, that you shall."

Then she anointed Ruth's body until it gleamed like gold and was fragrant as a field of flowers. And she put perfume upon the garments of Ruth.

And when Ruth stood dressed and beautiful as a dream, Naomi said proudly: "Go now to your beloved, my daughter, and tell him your love and he will tell you his!"

But Ruth stood still and bethought herself; and then she took from her pocket the golden amulets she wore when she first came into Judah, each bearing the figure of Ashtar crowned with stars and a crescent moon and offering her full round breasts. And Ruth went to the mirror and put the amulets upon her brow. "In Moab these were said to have potent magic with men," she said; and their golden glitter danced seductively above the darkness of her eyes.

But Naomi went to her and took them off. "You have no need for Moabite magic, my child. You have what is better than any amulet—your God-given beauty, which the good Lord made for the enchantment of men."

And she led Ruth to the broken door. And they heard again the merry voices of the men of Boaz singing:

> *Behold, thou art fair, my love;*
> *behold, thou art fair;*
> *Thine eyes are as doves. . . .*

And Naomi kissed Ruth and said: "Go now, my daughter."

And as Ruth veiled her face and went out into the falling night and mounted her milk-white donkey the round harvest moon hung over the hills of Judah in full golden splendor.

The rising moon shone through the flying chaff which rose up in an iridescent cloud as the men of Boaz threshed and winnowed the last of the barley, driving their teams of great bullocks and oxen over the grain on the threshing floor and tossing it up into the evening wind.

And the moonlight shone on the bare bodies of the strong men, led by Gibbor who lifted up his voice in song. And lustily the men sang as they labored:

> There are threescore queens,
>   And fourscore concubines,
>   And virgins without number.
> But my dove, my undefiled is one,
>   The only one of her mother . . .
>   The pure one of her that bare her.
>
> The women all saw her,
>   And called her blessed.
> Yea, the queens and the concubines
>   All praised her.

And at the end of their song a mighty shout rose up from the men.

And Boaz went riding Yohfe among them in high good humor, praising them for the fine harvest they had made of the crops the good Lord had given him, and seeing to the lighting of the fires and the preparation of the food and the opening of many wineskins for their feasting when they had finished. And when Boaz saw that one of the oxen on the threshing floor had been muzzled he bade its driver unmuzzle the beast.

"But it will eat of the grain," said Elias who stood over the threshers urging them on to the end of their labor.

Boaz said: "Let the beast eat. Is it not worthy of plentiful food for its labor? And did not Moses say: *Thou shalt not muzzle the ox that treadeth out the corn.* Let it eat! Let us all eat and drink and be merry."

When they had finished the threshing and heaped up the good grain the men washed their bronzed and sweated bodies in the nearby brook, with loud shouts of laughter as they splashed each other.

And Boaz got down from his horse and tethered it to a cedar tree and went to the brook to wash among his men; and he washed the wound on his brow which had healed; and he raised up his eyes to the moonlit hills and the heavens and said as he wiped the muscles of his arms: "Blessed art thou, O Lord our God, King of the universe, who has sanctified us by Thy commandments, and has commanded us concerning the washing of the hands."

Then Boaz and his men gathered about the fires, the roasting corn and the meat, and ate heartily as strong men do after hard labor and drank the wine that warmed and cheered them. "To life!" they said to each other as they lifted the bulging goatskins, letting the dark blood-red wine spurt in a shining stream down into their gullets. And they talked as they ate the hot pungent food and drank the cool fragrant wine, their eyes and their faces gleaming and their voices rising in the fire-and-moonlit air as they boasted of their prowess in that day's fighting before Jerusalem the city of the Jebusites. And Boaz, sitting among them with cool-eyed Elias on his right hand and hairy-handed Gibbor on his left, raised up his voice above the voices of his men and said:

"Hear now the blessing of our father Jacob on Judah his son which is coming to pass in our time:"

And all the men were silent and listened to Boaz:

> *Judah, thee shall thy brethren praise:*
> > *Thy hand shall be on the neck of thine enemies;*
> > *Thy father's sons shall bow down before thee.*
> *Judah is a lion's whelp;*
> > *From the prey, my son, thou art gone up:*
> *He stooped down, he couched as a lion,*
> > *And as a lioness; who shall rouse him up?*
> *The sceptre shall not depart from Judah,*

> *Nor the ruler's staff from between his feet,*
> *Till he come to Shiloh,*
>   *Having the obedience of the peoples.*
> *Binding his foal unto the vine,*
>   *And his ass's colt unto the choice vine;*
> *He hath washed his garments in wine,*
>   *And his vesture in the blood of grapes:*
> *His eyes shall be red with wine,*
>   *And his teeth white with milk.*

Then Boaz drank deeply of the wine which Gibbor handed to him.

And Elias said: "But though this day the hand of Judah has been on the neck of his enemies, the scepter is not yet in the hands of Judah, and until we have a strong ruler in Judah having the obedience of all Israel we shall have no peace from our enemies, the Jebusites and the Moabites and the Philistines, who lie in wait for us to gather our crops as did the Midianites in the days of Gideon."

Then Gibbor took again the wineskin from which he had already drunk much wine and he stood up and drank again so copiously that the dark wine spilled down from his mouth on to his hairy chest and his garments, and he said drunkenly to Elias: "See! *He hath washed his garments in wine.* That much at least has come to pass in our time. And Boaz is right in not wanting to rule over Israel for then as he has so wisely said it will no longer be true that every man does what is right in his own eyes. So let every man drink until, as our father Jacob well said, *His eyes shall be red with wine.*" And he offered the wineskin to Elias.

But Elias spurned the wine, saying scornfully:

> *Like a city broken down and without a wall,*
> *So is he whose spirit is without restraint.*

And Gibbor answered him drunkenly saying: "A strong man wants no restraint, nor have we any need of walled cities. Did we not beat the Jebusites back behind their great walls?"

And the men all shouted: "That we did this day!" and they all turned from their eating and drinking to listen to Gibbor, who said: "And did not Gideon rout the great host of Midianites and Amalekites with but three hundred picked men? That was a fine trick he played on them, was it not—frightening all that host unto flight in the night with the blowing of trumpets and the breaking of pitchers that held burning torches. Ha-ha! *They stood every man in his place round about the camp: and all the host ran: and they shouted and put them to flight. And they blew the three hundred trumpets, and the Lord set every man's sword against its fellow in all that host and the host fled as far as Beth-Shittah toward Zererah, as far as the border of Abelmeholah, by Tabbath. And the men of Israel were gathered together out of Naphtali, and out of Asher, and out of all Manasseh, and pursued after Midian. And Gideon sent messengers throughout all the hill country of Ephraim, saying, Come down against Midian, and take before them the waters, as far as Beth-barah, even Jordan. So all the men of Ephraim were gathered together, and took the waters as far as Beth-barah, even Jordan. And they took the two princes of Midian, Oreb and Zeeb; and they slew Oreb at the rock of Oreb, and Zeeb they slew at the wine press of Zeeb, and pursued Midian: and they brought the heads of Oreb and Zeeb to Gideon beyond Jordan.* And that was not all they brought Gideon. They brought him the golden earrings out of their spoil, a thousand and seven hundred shekels of gold, and though Gideon would not be king he lived like a king to a good old age in his own house, with many wives, and they say he begat threescore and ten sons of his body, which I would rather do than be king—not to speak of his concubine in Shechem by whom he begat Abimelech who did become king and reigned but three years until his head was crushed by a millstone dropped upon him by a woman from the tower of the city of Thebez. So I say that our Boaz is right and wise in not wanting to rule over Israel. But let him lead us against our enemies and let him live without restraint off the fat of the land and take all the women he wants." And a hearty shout for Boaz rose up from the men and they returned to their eating and drinking about the fires, and their hearts were merry and they boasted of their prowess with women and they lifted their voices and sang:

> Come, my beloved, let us go forth into the field;
> Let us lodge in the villages.
> Let us rise up early to the vineyards;
> Let us see if the vine hath budded. . . .

And when their song had ended cool-eyed Elias said to Boaz: "Thank the Lord, my friend, that you have come through this year's journey to Shiloh safe not only from the weapons of our enemies but from the wiles of our women, the daughters of the merchants who seek each year in the harvest to ensnare you with your fat lands and to end the free life you now live in your fields."

But Boaz laughed aloud and said: "Fear not for me, Elias; for though I do not look with dislike upon women as you do, yet do I cherish my freedom as much as do you —this freedom to eat and to drink when and whatever I choose, and to sleep where I wish—as I shall sleep tonight here under the moon-and-starlit sky. And I mean to keep this freedom for a while." And he took the wineskin from Gibbor and drank deeply from it. Then Boaz said: "And when I do take a woman to wife it will not be one whose rich father sells her to me like a slave; nor will I be tricked into marriage as Jacob was tricked by Laban into marrying Leah; but I shall marry only a woman of my own choosing as Jacob took Rachel, because he loved her."

Elias said: "All the same I am content that the barley harvest is over and there will be no gleaners in the fields for a spell until the wheat harvest begins. Tomorrow we can do our ploughing in peace, with no women in the fields to distract either you or your men who have had little else in their thoughts all the harvest."

And the men about the fires were singing:

> *Behold, thou art fair, my love;*
> *behold, thou art fair;*
> *Thine eyes are as doves. . . .*

And Gibbor said to Elias: "Why don't you drink wine, Elias, and sing songs and cease worrying about the women?" And the voice of Gibbor was thick with the wine he had drunk.

And Elias said:

> *Wine is a mocker, strong drink a brawler,*
> *And whosoever gets reeling drunk is a fool.*

But Gibbor laughed and said: "And it would do you much good, Elias, if you went sporting with a woman. Wouldn't it, men?"

And the men sitting nearby them laughed aloud with Gibbor at Elias.

Elias said scornfully: "Our wise men have said: *Give not thy strength unto women.*"

And one of the men said: "Yet in our Book of Remembrance it is said that even our forefather Isaac was sporting with Rebekah when the king Abimelech discovered that they were man and wife."

Then Elias stood up from his place saying: "We start ploughing the fields at dawn, Boaz. Are you not ready for sleep?"

But Boaz, cheered by the wine he had drunk, was loath to lie down to sleep. And he raised up his voice and sang with the men:

> *Thy two breasts are like two fawns,*
> *That are twins of a roe*
> *Feeding among the lilies.*

And Elias called to the men to cease their singing and get them to sleep on the threshing floor.

And the men heeding him rose up and made their beds round about the fires and lay down to sleep. And Elias lay down with them.

But Gibbor said to Boaz: "This is too fine a night for sleeping. And there is yet much good wine to be drunk. So let us get good and drunk." And he raised up a wineskin and took a deep draught, and handed it to Boaz.

The night was indeed fine, with the full moon changing from gold to shining silver as it rose high in the sky; and the stars hung low like lamps swinging gently in the warm harvest wind.

So Boaz remained sitting by the fire and drank wine with Gibbor, who as they passed the wineskin between them took two draughts of the wine to one of Boaz; and Gibbor complained in his rambling talk of the austerity of men in Israel like Elias: "They take too strictly the words of old Moses who could not have foreseen all our needs here in this land. Now consider this matter of the one God of Israel." And he stopped for another long draught from the wineskin, which he then handed to Boaz. "It is not enough that we worship him, sacrifice to him, give thanks for what he has given us—but we must learn and keep all his laws: only then can we have a good life! Now I am an unlearned man. Is that fair to me?" And he took the wineskin from Boaz and drank deeply again.

Boaz said: "It is the duty of man to inform himself. Since man chose to have the knowledge of good and evil the responsibility for learning God's laws rests with him. And an ignorant man cannot be truly pious; for without understanding no man can truly worship his Creator."

And Gibbor said: "But I thought it was the woman Eve who chose to eat of the tree of the knowledge of good and evil! And who wants to be pious?" And he took another drink of the wine and handed it back to Boaz. "Now I do not deny that the Lord God of Israel is a mighty God. True, he did bring our fathers out of bondage in Egypt, performing great miracles for us there and at the Red Sea and in the desert. And true it is that more than once since then he has delivered us with a mighty hand from our enemies and even this very day from the Jebusites when he helped you with that storm over Jerusalem, which was indeed a great help." And he stopped again for a draught of the wine which he took from the hand of Boaz. "But when it comes to such things as crops the Lord our God has not been so reliable. Though he promised Moses that we would be blessed here in the field, in the fruit of our ground and our cattle, yet have we had famine in this land, so that men of Israel have gone out of the land even as far as Moab—as did Elimelech and his two sons." And he raised up the wineskin and drank again and returned it to Boaz, saying: "Drink!"

And Boaz drank and he said: "But that has been because of the backsliding of the children of Israel, when they have not observed the statutes of the Lord God of Israel which Moses set down for us, and have gone awhoring after strange gods. Then we have been punished just as the Lord God had warned us."

And Gibbor taking the wineskin again said: "There are those among us who think otherwise. There are those among us who think that the great famine came upon us because we had not served the Baalim of this land, who make it fertile for those who serve them. The Jebusites had no famine, nor did the Moabites. And so, last year some of us went up to the high place of the Jebusites; and though none of us went so far as did some of the Jebusites who in their great drunkenness did mutilate their manhood, which was going too far, I thought, even for a good crop; and though only a few of us tried that foolishness with the priests in women's attire who were offering themselves to the men—we all did sacrifice to Baal and Ashtar on their altars, and see now the fine crops we have got; and who can say that the Baalim did not help us? And surely it can do no harm to serve all the gods—the Baalim of this land as well as the Lord God of Israel from Sinai!"

Then Boaz chided him saying: "We cannot limp on both sides—with Baal and the Lord God of Israel. Did you not hear this very day in Shiloh how the Lord God of Israel has commanded us saying: *Thou shalt have no other God before me*——"

"I know, I know," said Gibbor, impatient in his drunkenness. "I know he is a jealous God. And he is with us everywhere so that a man may not leave his own dung in a field for fear of offending him. The gods of other peoples remain upon their high places; but our God is too much with us, because he is a jealous God. And he dwells in a tabernacle of acacia wood and silver and gold with curtains of fine linen, while other gods dwell in stone pillars. And while they are served with whoring, our God has commanded us against the free taking of women although, as Zvuv says, he has no use for a woman himself. Just as you, Boaz, stopped me in the field from taking the beautiful Moabitess though you yourself did not take her. And the Lord our God made a terrible to-do in Israel over that concubine who was taken at Gibeah, so that to this very day we men of Benjamin have not enough women and can get none from among the daughters of the other tribes." And Gibbor drank deeply as if to drown his great grief.

And Boaz, his heart warm with wine, said gently to Gibbor: "Yet the Lord knows it is hard for a man to be denied the love of woman, for the Lord God himself said to Adam: *It is not good that the man should be alone,* and gave him Eve."

And Gibbor said: "Indeed it is not for nothing that the Lord put loins between a man's legs; and he cannot blame us for wanting the pleasure to be got from them."

And Boaz said: "The Lord God does not deny us anything. The Lord God tells man to deny himself only the evil that will destroy him."

And Gibbor complained: "The Lord God of Israel commands the men of Israel to deny themselves and each other all the women and the wine they want for their heart's content. And there you sit holding your wineskin yet not

drinking, Boaz, when you might be as drunk as I am."
And he took the wineskin from the hand of Boaz and
drank. "The trouble with you, Boaz, is that you have some
of the spirit of Elias in you, that self-denying spirit of
Moses; and like so many of our Israelites you never get
drunk enough. Drink, Boaz, your eyes are not yet red."
And he handed the wineskin to Boaz. "And you might be
lying this night with any of the women of Bethlehem,
who would gladly come to the bed of rich Boaz, or you
might take the woman of Moab who is more beautiful
than any woman in Bethlehem and gleans in your field.
For she comes from a land where the women go up to the
high place in this season and offer themselves to their gods
and their men." Then Gibbor took the wine and drank
deeply again, and his eyes were very red with wine as he
looked into the eyes of Boaz, saying: "And if the Moabitess
came to you here this night and offered herself would
you not take her, Boaz?"

But Boaz said nothing; and he heard the breathing of
sleeping men on the threshing floor, the sound of the
restless beasts in their stalls, and of Yohfe cropping the
grass by the tree to which he was tethered.

And Gibbor said: "Surely you would. For I know you,
Boaz, from the days when I first came to Judah and we
were young lads together running about unrestrained like
wild colts in the fields. And you are in your heart as lustful as I."

And Boaz said: "Indeed I cannot deny my manly lust;
but I am no longer as unrestrained, Gibbor."

And Gibbor said: "But if the Moabitess came now in
the night you would surely take her. You would lose
your restraint as quickly as Yohfe there would break his
tether if a fine mare came into this field. And you would

be a fool if you did not, Boaz. And it must be very pleasant at this time of the year for a man to have women to come as they do in Moab and offer themselves instead of his having to pursue and to take them as we sons of Benjamin will do in the wine harvest when we shall go up to Shiloh and wait for the pretty daughters of Shiloh to come out in the vineyards and dance and we will lie in wait for them and each man will seize one for himself and carry her off and thus the fathers of Shiloh will not have broken their oath at Gibeah not to give their daughters to the men of Benjamin. Though it is a long time to wait until the wine harvest. But rest assured, Boaz, that I will take me the most beautiful of the maidens of Shiloh and many of them are very beautiful but none is so beautiful and desirable as Ruth the woman of Moab."

And Gibbor, having drunk deeply again from the wine-skin, lay down clasping it to him, embracing the bulging goatskin, and quickly fell fast asleep because of all the wine he had drunk.

Then Boaz covered up Gibbor, wrapping his cloak about him, for the fire had died; and then Boaz went apart from the sleeping men to lie leaning against a heap of winnowed grain. And the smell of the fertile seed was warm in his nostrils. And his heart and his loins were warm with the wine he had drunk. And Yohfe, his stallion, tethered under the nearby cedar came to Boaz and nuzzled him and blew his warm breath upon him. And Boaz stroked the horse's satin-smooth head, saying softly: "In one way Gibbor is right. In a way any beast is enviable: the wild one heeds no law but his own desire; the tame beast must heed the law of his master. The wild beast takes what he wants; and the tame one's need is taken care of. Neither one has either conscience or responsibility as man has in the presence of his maker. You, my fine handsome friend, are enviable in that you are not torn between your desires and your reason, for I, your master, do restrain you from the harmful or evil consequences your desires may bring. If I do not want you to bring the white mare of Elias to foal I do not command you saying: thou shalt not mount the mare of Elias. I tether you here where you cannot reach the mare in her stall. But the Lord God my master merely tells me the consequences and says, Take heed. He does not restrain nor prevent me; I must restrain myself, choosing often between conflicting counsels. I have been told:

> Look thou not upon the wine
> When it is red,
> When it giveth its color in the cup,
> When it goeth down smoothly:
>
> At the last it biteth like a serpent,
> And stingeth like an adder.
> Thine eyes shall behold strange things,
> And thine heart shall utter froward things.
> Yea, thou shalt be as he that lieth down in the midst
>   of the sea,
> Or as he that lieth upon the top of a mast.

And indeed it is so, as Gibbor well knows, and as I know also from the days when I was as thoughtless as Gibbor. And I know also that:

> A happy heart maketh a cheerful countenance;
> By sorrow the spirit is broken.

And I know that:

> A happy heart is good medicine
> But a broken spirit drieth up the bones.

249

And now my heart is happy and my loins lusty with the wine I have drunk and I am tempted to go on drinking until like Gibbor I lie prostrate and unfeeling, or to ride you up into Bethlehem and go awhoring among the harlots there. But I also remember the words of a godly man of Israel, my father Salmon, who said:

> *My son, give me thine heart,*
> *And let thine eyes delight in my ways:*
> *For a whore is a deep ditch;*
> *And a strange woman is a narrow pit. . . ."*

Boaz ceased speaking and Yohfe wandered away from him to crop again the moonlit grass. And Boaz lay still but awake. And his eyes resting upon the moonlit hills were filled with their entrancing beauty, yet were dreaming inwardly upon another entrancing beauty, the most desirable of all the beauty of the universe, the beauty of that strange woman of Moab. And in his ears were the slow, strangely sweet words that had flowed from her lips like honey when they stood and spoke together at Shiloh. And the wine-warmed heart and loins of Boaz were filled with an exaltation and a longing for glory and for beauty: he was great with the spirit of creation; at one with his God in the presence of the work of his Creator who had made the moon and the hills and had made him, Boaz, potent and powerful. For had he not vanquished a strong and hateful enemy that day with the help of the Lord? and had he not reaped a rich harvest with the help of the Lord? and now, like the Lord, he could create man in his own image if the woman he desired were there beside him. And the eyes of Boaz resting upon the moonlit hills were filled with the beauty of that strange woman of Moab until the soft sounds of the night—the sighing of balmy breezes, the endless croaking of frogs in the fields and, the ceaseless call of crickets, the measured breathing of sleeping men on the threshing floor—lulled him to sleep. . . .

Then out of the shadow of roadside trees a dreamlike figure emerged and came down a hill moving swiftly and silently across the field through the moonlit air, her feet glimmering white in the grasses.

And Ruth came and lay down at the feet of Boaz and covered herself with his cloak.

And Yohfe whinnied; and Boaz stirred and turned. He opened his eyes, and, startled, he said, "Who is there?"

"It is I. It is Ruth," she said softly.

"Who?"

"Naomi's Ruth."

And Boaz looked upon her with the unwondering enchantment of the dreamer who accepts what he dreams because it is what he wishes.

"Yes, it is Ruth!" he sighed happily, as she turned her head and the moonlight fell upon her face, and gleamed in the soft darkness of her eyes. "But why are you there at my feet?" he whispered.

"I have covered myself with thy cloak, Boaz. Thou hast been kind to me."

"But I do not want you at my feet. Rise up, Ruth," he said, "so that I may know that this is not but a dream."

And Ruth stood up before him.

And Boaz murmured:

> *How beautiful are thy feet in sandals, O prince's daughter!*
> *The joints of thy thighs are like jewels,*

The work of the hands of a cunning workman.
Thy navel is like a round goblet,
  Wherein no mingled wine is wanting:
Thy belly is like an heap of wheat
  Set about with lilies.

Thy two breasts are like two fawns that are twins of
    a roe;
Thy neck is like a tower of ivory;
Thine eyes as the pools in Heshbon. . . .

"Come here to me," he whispered, and she came to sit beside him, leaning against the grain. And he said: "I have looked at you often, from afar, Ruth, and found you very beautiful to behold; and I have listened to your strange speaking and found your voice very sweet to my ear; and now it is a wonderful, unspeakable delight to have you so near me here in the moonlight." And he put his hand gently upon her.

And Ruth said: "Nor can I speak, Boaz, of my delight to be here. When I left Moab with Naomi I knew only that I could not be happy there because my spirit had been weaned from the evil ways of Moab and was forever married to the spirit of Naomi's people—of thy people."

"And are you happy among us?"

"It is not always pleasant to be an alien, Boaz, a stranger in a strange land; to be looked upon sometimes with malice by the women and with wantonness by the men, and with suspicion by all in time of danger. But in thy fields I have found kindness; and now that I have come to thee I know that only with thee can I have the fullness of happiness."

"But you should not have come here in the night, Ruth. Have you not feared to come? What if you are seen? You know what will be said of you by the men here and by the women in Bethlehem. They will speak of the shamelessness of the women of Moab."

"Let them speak. Perhaps it is true that no good woman in Israel would do this, and that they will have reason to say: she is but a Moabite wanton. But thou art good, Boaz, and strong, and thou wilt protect me from all evil."

"But how do you know, Ruth, that I am good and will protect you from evil?"

"As I told thee at Shiloh: my heart tells me. And hast thou not protected me already? And dost thou know why, Boaz?"

"Because you are a stranger, Ruth."

"And because thou lovest me, Boaz," said Ruth softly. "And that is why I have not feared to come to thee in the night, to remind thee that thou art our near kinsman— Naomi's and therefore mine—and that it is thy right to redeem the land of Elimelech and to raise up again the name of the dead on his inheritance."

For a long moment Boaz said nothing, only looked with wonder at this woman who was like no woman he had ever known. And there was no sound between them but the cropping of Yohfe in the shadow of the nearby cedar and the sweet song of a nightingale in its branches. And Ruth said, "Is it unseemly to thee that I should tell thee of thy right to marry me, Boaz?"

"No, Ruth," he answered gently. "I love your courage as I love your beauty. But there is another man who is a closer kinsman than I. It is Tobias, the merchant, who has the first right to redeem the property of Elimelech."

"But him," said Ruth sadly, "I do not love."

Then Boaz smiled upon Ruth and took her into his

strong arms, saying: "And I too have sought the one whom I shall love as Jacob loved Rachel, for whom he labored twice seven years." And he murmured to Ruth:

> *Behold, thou art fair, my love;*
> * behold, thou art fair;*
> *Thine eyes are as doves.*
> *Behold, thou art fair, my beloved,*
> * Yea, pleasant;*
> *The beams of our house are cedars*
> *And our walls are cypress. . . .*

And he put his desirous hands upon her saying: "You are very beautiful, my beloved, white and golden and sweet, like milk and honey," he said, "Milk and honey! And it is a wonderful delight to breathe your fragrance with the fragrance of the harvest night." And he kissed her mouth, and murmured:

> *Honey and milk are under thy tongue;*
> *And the fragrance of thy garments*
> * is like the fragrance of Lebanon.*

And he kissed her long and his passion was strong in Boaz so that he was sorely tempted; but his love for Ruth was stronger even than his passion.

And when he lifted up his head he saw the stirring of a restless man on the threshing floor where the fires had died; and one thin pale line of light had appeared low down on the far horizon. And Yohfe pricked up his ears and whinnied.

And Boaz said: "You must go now, my beloved, for the dawn will be coming soon and you must not be seen here. In the morning I shall go up to Bethlehem and speak to Tobias of the redemption." And he raised her up to her feet, and he murmured:

254

Lo thou art all fair, my love,
And there is no blemish in thee. . . .

And Ruth said:

Set me as a seal upon thy heart,
As a seal upon thine arm. . . .

And Boaz saw in her dark eyes that the heart of Ruth was content and full to overflowing with love of him.

And Boaz said: "Take some of this winnowed grain in your cloak for Naomi"; and he helped her generously. "And go quickly now," he said; and he kissed her again and covered her face with her veil.

And as she went from him he stood by Yohfe, saying softly: "How like a dream! As if in a dream she came out of the darkness of my sleep into the soft moonlight. What ineffable joy and pride in her love and faith have come to me—uncalled—like a gift—from the harvest night. And I might have taken her, Yohfe—I might have taken that strange woman with her strange ways whose love would be unlike the love of any woman I have known. Why did I not take her? I did not take her because I love her, Yohfe; and even now if I followed her I could take her; and is it not strange that I do not go after her, Yohfe?" And he stroked the silken head of the restless stallion, whose warm breath blew upon him. "But you cannot know this love of man for woman; for though man can be beastly no beast can know what it is to be a man. But see there, Yohfe, how enchanting it is to watch her cross the field and ascend the hill, her white feet glimmering among the dark grasses, her shapely hips swaying so gracefully, her sturdy shoulders bowed under the burden of my gift, her lovely form merging now with the shadows of the tall trees by the roadside. How like a dream! . . ." And as

Boaz lay down again by the grain, deep sleep fell upon him and what he had seen and done became part of a long pleasant dream. . . .

Her milk-white donkey was tethered in the shadow of a tree by the moonlit road that wound up the steep hill to Bethlehem. And Ruth put her burden of grain upon the sleepy beast and mounted upon it and switched it lightly to rouse it, but the donkey did not stir. And a man ran up onto the road and came hastening to her through the patches of moonlight and shadow cast by the tall cypress trees by the roadside.

And she thought: "It is Boaz; and he has decided he will not wait for tomorrow." And Ruth sat upon the milk-white donkey and waited with fast-beating heart and fainting flesh for his approach; and her desire for the love of Boaz was very great. And she thought: "Now will I gladly give myself to Boaz whom I love. Did not Naomi say: 'He will tell you what you shall do.' "

And she lifted up her eyes to greet him as he came near; and she saw then that it was not Boaz but Gibbor, and he carried a wineskin and staggered with drunkenness. And Ruth was sorely frightened; and she switched her donkey hard, but the sleepy beast barely stirred.

And Gibbor came to her and put out his hairy hand and pulled the veil from her face. "I knew it was you," he said thickly. "There is no woman in the world has as pretty a walk as you have."

And Ruth said: "Let me go."

But he held to her donkey's head with one red-haired hand, and he swayed as he stood. "I see you've been gleaning," he said, looking at the burden of grain that she held before her. "Come glean with me, now, Ruth." And his eyes in the moonlight were hot and bloodshot. "Come drink wine and sport with me too, as the Moabites do."

"Let me go, Gibbor," she said, "or I shall call to Boaz that thou art molesting me. Boaz has said he will marry me."

And Gibbor laughed aloud. "So that's how it is! Well then you have got me to thank for getting him drunk or Boaz would not have said that."

And Ruth said: "It was not as thou thinkest, Gibbor; though if Boaz came now and asked it of me, I would go with him."

"Boaz is no better man than I am," said Gibbor. "I know Boaz well. His desire for you is no different from mine."

And Ruth said: "But Boaz did not take me when I went to him."

Then Gibbor stared at her, unbelieving: "Why not?"

"Because Boaz loves me," said Ruth.

And Gibbor's befuddled eyes looked upon Ruth in sore puzzlement; and he said: "Boaz did not take you because he loves you, and you would give yourself now to Boaz because he did not take you! What sort of nonsense is this?"

And Ruth said: "It is a woman's nonsense, Gibbor, which thou dost not understand. True, it is, that the lust in the flesh of Boaz is no different from thine, Gibbor; but thou lackest the love of his spirit. It is both that a woman wants. Any man's lust will give her a child. But only the lusty man who loves her will give her both joy and peace. Boaz desired to take me as thou dost; but Boaz wants to marry me because he loves me."

257

But drunken Gibbor did not heed her. He was entranced by the dark fire of her eyes in the cool beauty of her moonlit face. "I'll take you," cried Gibbor, "even if you won't give yourself to me," and he put his strong arm about Ruth to draw her down to him.

But Ruth raised up her switch and lashed his face twice, and the face of her donkey, which kicked up its heels and sent Gibbor sprawling and scampered away up the road.

The sun came up; and with it the host of familiar sounds of a workaday world: the incessant twitter of birds from field and wood, the crowing of cocks from the barnyard, the lowing of cattle, the bark of dogs, the braying of donkeys, and the stir of waking men from the threshing floor, among whom Elias went shouting: "Arise and shine for the light has come!"

The sun rose up like a clamorous brazen shield above the distant menacing hills of Moab, dispelling the enchanting darkness from the land and the seductive dreams from the mind of Boaz, as he woke and watched its rays glittering on the waters of the brook that ran gaily down the valley to the east, ran heedlessly down and away to the dead Salt Sea. And into the mind of Boaz crept a faint perturbation, seeped in and eddied about and rose up to wash away all the joy of the night in a flood of anxiety. Small doubts assailed him like a multitude of darting arrows—the immemorial doubts of a man in the face of marriage. But he brushed them aside; they fell away from before the vision of Ruth that rose again to his eyes and filled his heart with desire.

Before him the sun, shining on his wide fields, drew

258

up to his nostrils the smell of the rich warm soil. From behind him drifted the acrid smoke of the crackling fires and the noise of his young men preparing their food— with their hearty laughter and their free talk, boasting as ever of their prowess, in the harvest, in yesterday's combat, in amorous conquest.

And Boaz went down to the brook and washed in the clear cold water that routed all dreams and desires.

And cool-eyed Elias came and waited beside him, looking curiously upon him as Boaz dried himself and said the prayer—not with his eyes raised proudly to the hills this time, but uneasily downcast before the scrutiny of Elias as he hastily murmured: "Blessed art thou . . . King of the Universe . . . sanctified . . . commanded . . . washing of hands."

"Did you sleep well, Boaz?" asked Elias.

"Yes—no, that is——" said Boaz, and he stopped speaking.

For Gibbor and another young man were coming down to the brook. And Gibbor's face bore two scarlet welts. ". . . and when I opened my eyes," he was saying, "I'm a son of Belial if I did not see a beautiful young woman walking up toward the road in the moonlight. And she looked as if she had been gleaning because she carried a bundle of grain." And Gibbor stood nearby and glanced at Boaz and continued to speak as he prepared to wash. "And then I bethought me how foolish that was because no woman would go gleaning in the night—long after midnight—that is, not by picking it up in the field—and how she must have got it from someone she had been with."

"Well, and did you go after her?" asked the other eagerly.

259

Then Elias spoke to Boaz saying: "It will be a fine day for the ploughing."

But Boaz was listening to Gibbor.

And Gibbor said: "Indeed I did," and he looked again upon the face of Boaz that was darkening with anger, saying: "But in my haste I ran into some low hanging branches and cut my face and fell. And by the time I got up to the road she was gone."

"Just a dream!" mocked the other. "As it is said of them that tarry long at the wine: *Thine eyes shall see strange things*."

And Gibbor said: "Not so! She was real enough. Though she had her face veiled, I would know that shape anywhere. There are not two like her in this land. It was the Moabitess. I knew she could be taken, the very first time that I saw her."

Then Boaz turned upon him. "You lie, Gibbor!" he said with a furious voice.

And Gibbor said: "You mean she was not on the threshing floor last night? How do you know she was not?"

And Boaz said: "I mean that she is a virtuous woman."

And Gibbor said: "Then what was she doing down here in the night? And who gave her the grain she carried away? Perhaps if she came in the night to you, Boaz, you would restrain yourself, but I can assure you there are other men here who are not so restrained. And I suppose you will be telling me that the women of Moab do not offer themselves every spring in the grove of their high place and——"

But Boaz had knocked Gibbor down with a blow, and his mouth was bleeding. "You left-handed son of Belial!" cried Boaz. "You will work no more on this land! Truly our father Jacob said: *Benjamin is a wolf that raventh.* Go now!"

And Gibbor, crestfallen, got up and went and mounted upon his donkey and scampered away up the hill to Bethlehem.

Then Boaz said brusquely to Elias: "Now get the men started. I must ride up to Bethlehem this morning." And he turned away to go to where Yohfe was tethered.

And Elias said: "Will you not eat first?"

Boaz said: "No, I cannot eat now. I must go right away. Get them started." And he went for his horse.

And Elias shouted to the men to start ploughing. "Wait one moment!" he called after Boaz, who was mounting upon Yohfe.

And Boaz reined in the restless horse and waited.

Elias went to Boaz. "I saw the woman, also," he said.

"Well?" said Boaz.

And Elias said: "Is it because of her that you are going to Bethlehem?"

Boaz said: "Yes, it is because of her."

And Elias said: "She has bewitched you, Boaz."

And Boaz said: "Well, then she has bewitched me. But that does not make Ruth an enemy of Israel. Nor does that make her any worse than the women of Bethlehem; she has merely succeeded where others have failed."

"Listen, my friend," said cool-eyed Elias. "Yesterday, after finishing a fine harvest you ate with gusto and drank heartily, you made merry with your men boasting of your liberty, and you lay down to rest, satisfied, without a care —as carefree as the youngest of them. And here you are, overnight, sorely troubled, at odds with the best of your workers, and in a fair way to lose this precious peace and freedom—because of a woman."

Boaz said: "I am going to Bethlehem to see her nearest kinsman, Tobias, who will doubtless want——"

"Do not go, Boaz," Elias said earnestly. "Why go up to

Bethlehem? For years you escaped the scheming of the men of Bethlehem and their women, all their wiles and their offers, continued to live this fine, free life on your own land, among your men. And now in the harvest, in your own field, you let yourself be bewitched and captured by a strange woman! It is not only the Moabite women who offer themselves; all women offer themselves to men whom they wish to capture. Admit that she took you by surprise."

And Boaz said: "Yes, I was startled, Elias—aroused in the night to find her at my feet—that strange, courageous woman, with her sturdy bearing, the dark undaunted eyes in her fair face, the roundness of her warm, sunburnt arms. How those cats in the town will squall when they hear that she came here to me in the night, alone! She followed the prompting of her heart; in her straightforward fashion she came to me without fear. 'I am Ruth,' she said softly in the moonlight and took my heart. Yes, Elias, I was carried away, I was captured."

And cool-eyed Elias said: "But now you can forget all about it. Do not go up to Bethlehem, Boaz. She will not be coming to glean for a while; and nothing more need come of last night—if you do not go up."

Boaz looked gravely down upon urgent Elias. Then he said: "I have given my word. I must go." And he turned his horse's head and dug his heels into the burnished flanks of Yohfe and rode off at a breakneck gallop.

But as Yohfe climbed the hill toward the wall of the city with its two stone towers, the round and the square, glittering in the morning sunlight, Boaz let the reins droop and his pace slackened.

"Be-witched and cap-tured, Yohfe! That's what I have been," he murmured. "Be-witched and cap-tured! . . ." The words of Boaz fell to the beat of the horse's hoofs. "And why did she not come to me in the day, but in the night, after I had eaten and drunk and made merry? Be-witched and cap-tured! Baal take it!" He slapped the reins and the lagging horse hastened on. "Anyway nothing is settled yet. I have still to see Tobias. That grasping merchant is a shrewd bargainer. And if I show an interest in the long-neglected property of Elimelech, Tobias will surely hold out for a good profit on his right to redeem it. And that will let me out." And the reins fell slack in his hands. "That is, to be sure, if I really want to get out of it, Yohfe." The hoofbeats lagged again. And Boaz remembered her upturned face in the moonlight, the sweet warmth of her lips: "Like milk and honey," the graceful swing of her hips as she walked, her glimmering feet in the grass: "Milk and honey," he murmured, "Be-witched and cap-tured! And how, Yohfe my beauty, is a man to know his love from his lust since a man does not love a woman without lust, which stirs him first. Be-witched and cap-tured! Be-witched and cap-tured by an alien woman! What do I know of her strange ways and desires—disturbing my life, ending this fine freedom. And it is true that in Moab the women do give themselves freely in the spring; although she did say to Naomi, 'Thy people shall be my people and thy God my God!' But who can rely upon what a woman says, Yohfe? Be-witched and cap-tured! Only yesterday my spirit was at peace, and now—Be-witched!"

Yohfe had stopped and was nibbling a tuft of grass in the middle of the road.

"Baal take it!" cried Boaz: "But I gave her my word.

263

I said I would go to Tobias." And Boaz spurred the horse, which sprang to life and galloped on up the road to the city gates.

"It appears that love," said Tobias maliciously, "is not only blind but deaf."

They were seated in the house of Tobias, in the very room where Boaz had first seen Ruth, standing in the dark doorway which was now open to the warm sunny day.

And Boaz, sitting impatiently on the edge of his chair at the end of the long table, said: "I have no wish to hear your proverbs, Tobias. All that I wish to hear is whether you want to redeem the property of Elimelech and Mahlon his son."

"Indeed," said Tobias, his beady eyes fixed upon the troubled face of Boaz, "I have been considering redeeming that property. I talked to Naomi about it yesterday on the way back from Shiloh. And I, also, although I am not so young as you, have an eye not only for that property but for the pretty woman that goes with it."

And Boaz said: "Then why have you not taken your right?"

"For two reasons," said Tobias, eying him warily, "and I shall tell you my second reason first. It is because I saw how you looked upon Ruth all the way up to Shiloh, and it occurred to me then that you might be willing to pay a good price for my right to redeem the property of Elimelech. And, as enchanting as the Moabitess is, I am frank to say that, at my age, a good bargain would give me more satisfaction. Tell me now, Boaz. How much would you be willing to pay? Would three thousand shekels be too much?

264

That is just about what I lost because of your judgment against me in the court."

But Boaz sat still as if downcast and said nothing.

Then Tobias said to provoke him: "Perhaps I was mistaken, Boaz. Perhaps the presence of those Moabite marauders in Jerusalem and that battle with the Jebusites has shaken your interest in the woman of Moab. Perhaps you are not truly certain that you want the Moabite woman. Do you or do you not?"

"That is not your concern," said Boaz. "In any event I would not buy her like a slave. And if she will take you because you have the right, then let her. But I do not think that she will." And he stood up to go.

"Ah!" said Tobias, leaning back and stroking his paunch, as he looked shrewdly at Boaz. "I'm afraid you are right. And that being so I may as well tell you now my first reason for not having exercised my right to marry the Moabitess: I think she is no bargain."

"And what do you mean by that?" said Boaz angrily.

Tobias said: "Sit down, Boaz, and I will tell you."

And Boaz sat down.

And Tobias said slowly: "Now, as I was saying before, when you so rudely stopped me: love is not only blind but deaf, or you would know what I mean. Every man to his own taste, to be sure, and she is not to mine." And he paused then, watching Boaz carefully.

"And what," asked Boaz, "do *you* find wrong with Ruth?"

Tobias said: "She is too independent, for one thing. A woman's place, my dear Boaz, is in her home; and if I had my way it would be in the harem as it is among other peoples. We Israelites have long been prone to encouraging independence in our women, extolling those strong-minded matriarchs like Sarah, Rebekah, and Rachel, who took things in their own hands, and making heroines of Deborah and Jael. It sets a bad example. I would not want my daughter, Reba, to behave that way. She will make a much better wife as she is." Tobias looked toward the open door.

And Boaz could see Reba in the sunlit courtyard, where Yohfe was tethered. She was feeding sweets to his horse.

"I came here to speak of Ruth," said Boaz impatiently.

"To be sure," said Tobias. "What I meant to say is that Naomi is of that old generation of strong-willed women. She knows too much for a woman and has doubtless trained her strange daughter-in-law well in our laws and our ways so that the Moabitess might make her way into the congregation of the Lord."

And Boaz said: "Surely you do not think that Naomi would bring Ruth to sojourn among us unless she were weaned from the ways of Moab and steadfastly minded to become a true woman of Israel."

Tobias shrugged his fat shoulders and said: "Be that as it may, yet am I moved to say to you, Boaz, what the parents of Samson said to him when he wanted the Philistine woman of Timnah: *Is there not a woman among the daughters of thy brethren?*" And he looked out again to the courtyard where his daughter Reba still loitered by Boaz' stallion; but seeing that Boaz would give no heed to her, Tobias continued with yet more malice on his tongue: "And this young woman from Moab has got herself talked about in Bethlehem with her independence, boldly going down to the fields and doing a peasant's work. Immodesty, some people call it; and I may as well tell you that some have been saying worse things; early this morning Zvuv went up and down the streets shouting about the shameless abominations of Moab in our midst; and your man Gibbor came to tell me how late last night Ruth was seen——"

And Boaz stood up so violently that his chair upset.

"But, Boaz," cried Tobias, "I mean no offense; I am only telling you what is being said. To be sure, I know that this may be nothing but jealous gossip, and it is not nearly so important as——"

"As what?" demanded Boaz. "Tell me. I want to know all that there is to know about her."

"You should, to be sure," said Tobias, "if you are thinking of marrying her. But sit down, Boaz."

And Boaz picked up his chair and sat down.

"Now for my own part," the crafty old man went on, "I do not mind telling you why this young woman, though she is very handsome, is not to my taste. She is too sturdy. For my own part, I prefer them like our Bethlehem damsels—soft—you know—and very sweet. I admit that tastes differ. But aside from that, I must say that I do not see how you can look with pleasure on the prospect of having Naomi as your mother-in-law. I need hardly tell you that Bethlehem mothers-in-law are notorious, and Naomi is famous among them. A most determined old woman. And you, Boaz, should know what a determined woman can do, remembering that one in your own family—Tamar who deceived and seduced Judah into giving her a son. I am not saying that Naomi is not a noble old woman and has had a hard time; but she is much too crafty. To be sure, she cannot be blamed for wanting a good home and the name of her husband and son preserved in Judah; and when a man is in love he doesn't mind so much being taken in; but truly, Boaz, the manner in which she set out to get a good match for her outlandish daughter-in-law—egging her on—everyone here has been speaking of it. It may be a pretty chance, my dear Boaz, that the bewitching Moabitess came to glean in your fields, but there are people in Bethlehem, I must tell you, who think differently. To be sure, for my own part I would not go so far as to say, as some do, that Naomi induced her to come here from Moab for the sole purpose of hooking a man to——"

But Boaz upset his chair again, and this time he leaned across the table, his gray eyes agleam, and grasped Tobias, saying: "I will break every bone——"

"But Boaz," cried frightened Tobias, "you said that you wanted to know—— You can have the right, Boaz, for nothing! Whenever you want it. I will go with you to the gates and gather ten of the elders and hand you my shoe in token that the right of redemption is yours if you want her. I swear that I meant no harm, Boaz—just trying to tell you what——"

Then Boaz let go of the trembling old man: "You may keep the rest of your slanders for mean men like yourself—weak, despicable creatures, fearful of a strong woman!" And he went out of the door, slamming it shut behind him.

And Reba, seeing his wrathful face, fled into the house from before him.

Boaz mounted his horse and rode slowly through the narrow cobbled streets of the city, crowded with men and women and children, on foot, on donkeys and mules and camels, on their way to the market place by the gates of the city. And mingled with the rising tumult of the teeming traffic rose the doubts of Boaz: "And how is it within my own heart, Yohfe? Do I want my own woman strong? Do I not fear this strange woman because she is fearless and may be boldly deceiving me even as Rebekah deceived blind Isaac? And love, they say, is blind. And what if Tobias is telling the truth, Yohfe? Bewitched and hooked!" he muttered. "That is what I have been—hooked! I have suspected it all along, and that is what has been troubling me. They are no better than all the rest, Yohfe—scheming women: setting their traps—first to catch a man's eye and then his heart. Scheming all the time. What of last night? Doubtless Naomi prepared Ruth, instructing her. . . . 'Wait, my daughter, until he has eaten and drunk and his heart is merry, and——' That damnable Tobias was right. I have been blind and deaf: hooked by determined women into preserving the inheritance of Elimelech and raising up the name of Mahlon. But I will not let myself be taken in. I will go to them now and charge them openly. They will not dare deny it."

And he spurred Yohfe impatiently, saying: "Get on, my beauty; we must settle this matter by sundown; for it is the eve of the Sabbath and tomorrow you and I alike shall have rest and peace." But his way to the city gates across the crowded market place was halted again and again by oxcarts of vegetables, high-piled caravans, and herds of bleating sheep driven in from the countryside.

And as Boaz slowly approached the city gates he saw in the shade of the square stone tower of the Gate of the Judges the eldest of the three judges of Bethlehem sitting in judgment with one hand cupped to his ear and disposing calmly and quickly, one after another, of the cases coming before him. And Boaz envied the venerable old man, half blind and hard of hearing, the assurance with which he knew and spoke his judgment; and Boaz wondered how he who was now so undecided, so torn between heart and head, could ever again sit in judgment on others. "And who knows, Yohfe, but that I have dealt wrongly with Gibbor," he murmured. "For is it not said:

> *He that is slow to anger is better than the mighty;*
> *And he that ruleth his spirit is mightier than he that*
>   *taketh a city."*

And as Boaz came near to the gates he heard the harsh angry voice of Zvuv who stood in the shade of the round brick tower, arrayed in his ragged robe with graven tablets on brow and arm, berating the men who sat in the wineshops watching the women go by:

> *The commandment is a lamp,*
>   *and the teaching is a light,*
> *And reproofs of instruction are the way to life,*
> *To keep thee from the evil woman,*
> *From the smoothness of the alien tongue.*
> *Lust not after her beauty in thy heart.*
> *Neither let her captivate thee with her eyelids . . .*

And a voice called: "Boaz!" and out of the throng cool-eyed Elias came riding on his snow-white mare and stopped before him.

"What are you doing here?" demanded Boaz.

And Elias said: "I have come to get another man in the place of Gibbor," but his eyes moved uneasily from the grave eyes of Boaz.

And Boaz said: "Find Gibbor and tell him to return."

"But, Boaz———" began Elias.

And Boaz said: "Though Moses said: *Thou shalt surely rebuke thy neighbor,* did he not also say: *Thou shalt not take vengeance nor bear any grudge against the children of thy people but thou shalt love thy neighbor as thyself.*

And who am I to judge Gibbor? Am I better than he? Are his lustful desires any different from mine? Go find him, Elias."

"But Gibbor is gone," said Elias. "He is on his way back to Gibeah in Benjamin, to gather his brothers for the raid on the women of Shiloh when they come out to the vineyards in the wine harvest."

Boaz said: "It was a grave injustice we did to the men of Benjamin, to deny them women. For surely as the Lord God said of Adam—*It is not good that the man should be alone.*"

And cool-eyed Elias said: "It is not so for me; nor is it that which concerns me now." And he looked uneasily upon the troubled face of his friend and said: "What have you done here, Boaz?"

Boaz said: "I have been to see Tobias."

And Elias said: "Well, what did he say?"

Boaz said: "He has given me the right to redeem the property of Elimelech, but——"

"But now," said cool-eyed Elias, "you are going to those women."

"Yes," said Boaz, "but——"

And Elias said: "But have you considered that Naomi must have known very well that Tobias was her nearest kinsman; yet she sent Ruth to you?"

Boaz said: "I had not considered that, but——"

And Elias said: "But you are bewitched and hooked, my friend, entangled in the web old Naomi has woven for you with that young woman of Moab, as Delilah the Philistine woman wove into her web the hair of Samson the Strong. Do not go to them, Boaz," he pleaded. "If you do not go to them now, nothing more will happen."

And the harsh voice of Zvuv rising above the sound of

the multitude came to them from the Gate of the Wineshops:

> *Can a man take fire in his bosom*
> *And his clothes not be burned?*

And anger flared in the grave gray eyes of Boaz. "I will thank you to tend to your business, my friend, and leave me to mine. I judge no one on hearsay, neither man nor woman. I am going to get the truth of this matter for myself." And he turned the head of his horse away from Elias and rode out of the city gate.

Yet as he rode along the stony path that ran close outside the walls the doubts of Boaz continued to plague him: "Bewitched and hooked, Yohfe! Think of the peace I had yesterday, and now this gnawing suspicion. . . ."

And a prayer burst aloud from the lips of the tormented man: "O Lord, our God, King of the Universe, grant me that peace again."

He had come to the house of Naomi on its knoll outside of the city. Flowers and vines covered its cracked walls, but the broken door still stood part way open.

And as Boaz tethered Yohfe by the door he looked down from the neglected land of Elimelech to his own fertile fields in the valley below where his men were peacefully ploughing the good earth.

He heard the shuttling of a loom within the house, and the voice of Naomi called to the kitchen: "Watch the bread carefully, Ruth; a man likes good bread."

Boaz stood on the threshold and listened.

Naomi worked at her weaving a while, beating the weft

272

with the pin to make the web firm, and then called again to Ruth: "Did you do as I told you?"

"I did just as thou didst tell me, Naomi." The sweet voice of Ruth came from the kitchen, with the warm smell of baking bread. "He said he would speak to Tobias to-day."

And Naomi said confidently: "Be assured, my daughter, that he will not rest until he has settled the matter"; and she leaned back to admire her intricate weaving.

"Crafty old woman!" Boaz murmured to Yohfe. "Crafty weaver of webs for men. It is indeed true that I have not rested. And now I want rest and peace from the torment-ing business of this day. Now I shall go in and get it over with. I shall go in and say to them what I know." And he went into the house.

"See now who is here!" cried Naomi, when she lifted her eyes from her weaving and saw Boaz before her. "This very moment I had you in mind, Boaz, and spoke of you to Ruth!"

"The door being open," said Boaz, "I heard what you said."

Naomi looked up into his troubled eyes and she smiled: "The wise men say that even a husband should knock at the door when he is not expected."

Boaz said: "But you did expect me, Naomi. And you were right: I have not rested. And now I have come to tell you——"

"Sit down first, Boaz," said Naomi. "You look weary. Ruth is baking bread for the Sabbath. She made fine flour of the grain you gave her. Her bread smells good, does it not?"

And she called to Ruth: "Boaz is here; come and speak to him."

273

And Ruth answered: "In a moment. I cannot leave the bread."

"I knew you would come, Boaz," said Naomi, resuming her weaving.

And Boaz, still standing before her, said firmly, above the sound of her swift-darting shuttle: "Naomi, I have come to say that you and Ruth——"

But Naomi, without ceasing her weaving, said again: "Sit down, Boaz, and wait for her."

And Boaz continued louder: "——that I know you have planned this, that I——"

But Naomi, heedless of him, gently musing, as if weaving her words into the cloth she was making, said: "Having been the wife of one man and the mother of two I know very well by now the proud nature of man."

"I know," Boaz persisted, "that I have been bewitched into giving up——"

"Since the time of our mother Eve," mused Naomi, "men have blamed women for giving them what they most wanted." And she suddenly stopped her weaving. "Now look at me, Boaz!"

She raised her face up to his; and he saw how it was lined with furrows, worn like tracks in an ancient road, as if ridden by recurring sorrows.

Naomi said: "Surely, I sent her down to you. And surely, Boaz, I knew that Tobias was our nearest kinsman. But I knew that Tobias did not wish to marry Ruth. So the right is yours, Boaz."

And in the patient old eyes of Naomi, Boaz saw little of craft but much of wisdom—of knowledge of the needs of man and of the perversity of his proud nature.

Naomi said: "I will draw you a cup of wine, Boaz," and she went to a jar in the corner of the quiet room. And as the wine came gurgling from the spout the sweet voice of Ruth rose up in song in the kitchen as she drew out her loaves from the oven:

A woman of valor who can find?
  For her worth is far above rubies.
The heart of her husband trusteth in her,
  And he shall lack for nothing.
She doeth him good and not evil
  All the days of her life.
She seeketh out wool and flax
  And worketh well with her hands.
She is like the fine ships
  Bringing food from afar. . . .

Then the song sank to a wordless humming, and Naomi called again: "Are you coming, Ruth?"

And the sweet voice answered: "In one moment."

And Naomi brought Boaz the cup of wine and said: "Drink, Boaz, and rest." And she left him and went into the kitchen.

Boaz sat down and drank. And seeing the head of his faithful steed looking in at the open door, Boaz murmured: "They know very well, Yohfe, what will soften the heart of a man—wine and a song. But then, this patient woman who was a good mother to her sons and a faithful wife to Elimelech, this woman who went bravely with her men into a strange land and suffered their loss, does she not deserve a resting place in her old age? And who now can justly blame her for being determined; or even Tamar —but for whose determination I should not be here. And am I like Onan who hated to raise up the name of his own brother; and have I not said, like Moses, that all men are brothers? And yet, Yohfe—what of my cherished freedom —with this strange undaunted woman? . . ."

275

"Here is Ruth," said Naomi, for she had returned.

And there before Boaz stood Ruth, silent, expectant, holding a loaf of good bread in her brown hands; Ruth with her sweet mouth, her deep breast, the beauty of her young body—sturdy and straight as a cypress.

"I have brought you my bread, Boaz," she said.

And Boaz murmured:

> She is like the fine ships
> Bringing food from afar. . . .

And Naomi said:

> Houses and riches are inherited from fathers;
> But a prudent wife is a gift from God.

And Boaz said: "Where is her like in all of Judah?" And the spell of her eyes, dark and soft as the harvest night, was again upon him.

"Why have I resisted?" he cried to Naomi. "She is a mate for a prince!"

"She is better to me than seven sons," said Naomi, and she rolled up her weaving and put away the loom.

"Give me your hand, Ruth," said Boaz. "Joy and a great peace have enfolded me like a cloak, like the calm of the Sabbath to come."

"I love thee, too, Boaz," said Ruth. "And I say again unto thee as I said to Naomi: Whither thou goest I will go; thy people shall be my people and thy God my God."

And Boaz embraced her, saying, "Come, let us go to the Gate of the Judges and bring your near kinsman Tobias before ten of the elders, and he will say: 'Take my right of redemption; for I cannot redeem it.' And he shall draw off his shoe and give it to me as a sign, for this is the way in Israel. And I shall say unto the elders and unto all the

people: 'You are witnesses this day, that I have bought all
that was Elimelech's, and all that was Chilion's and Mahlon's, of the hand of Naomi. Moreover Ruth the Moabitess,
the wife of Mahlon, have I taken to be my wife, to raise
up the name of the dead upon his inheritance, that the
name of the dead be not cut off from among his brethren,
and from the gate of his place; you are witnesses this day!'
And all the people in the gate and the elders will say: 'We
are witnesses. The Lord make this woman that is come
into your house like Rachel and like Leah, which two did
build the house of Israel: and let your house be like the
house of Perez, whom Tamar bore unto Judah, of the
seed which the Lord shall give thee of this young woman.' "

And Naomi said: "She is worthy to be the mother of
kings," and she went away to the kitchen and left them
there alone.

Then Boaz said: "I do love you, Ruth, as I love my God,
with all my heart, with all my soul, and with all my might.
Praised be the Lord God of Israel," and he bowed his head
and kissed Ruth long and long. . . .

> . . . *So Boaz took Ruth, and she became*
> *his wife. And he went in unto her, and the*
> *Lord gave her conception, and she bare a*
> *son. . . . And Naomi took the child, and*
> *laid it in her bosom, and became nurse*
> *unto it. And the women her neighbors*
> *gave it a name, saying: There is a son born*
> *to Naomi; and they called his name Obed:*
> *He is the father of Jesse, the father of*
> *David.*

THE END OF THE STORY OF RUTH

Set in Linotype Baskerville
Format by A. W. Rushmore
Manufactured by The Haddon Craftsmen
Published by HARPER & BROTHERS, *New York*